GW00339014

HILL FARMER

A low, late autumn sun and a mist creeping down the dale throw an eerie light on a hill farm. In a landscape largely devoid of trees, Pennine farmsteads nestle in oases of sycamore and ash.

Neville Turner

HILL FARMER

*A working year
on the Fells*

First published in Great Britain 2001 by
Dalesman Publishing Company Limited
Stable Courtyard
Broughton Hall
Skipton
North Yorkshire BD23 3AZ
www.dalesman.co.uk

Text and photographs © Neville Turner BVM&S; MRCVS

A British Library Cataloguing in Publication record is available for
this book

ISBN 1 85568 186 2

Designed by Jonathan Newdick
Colour origination by Grasmere Digital Imaging Limited
Printed by Midas Printing (HK) Limited

All rights reserved. This book must not be circulated in any form
of binding or cover other than that in which it is published and
without similar condition of this being imposed on the subsequent
purchaser. No part of this publication may be reproduced, stored
on a retrieval system or transmitted in any form, or by any means,
electronic, mechanical, photocopying, recording or otherwise,
without either prior permission in writing from the publisher or a
licence permitting restricted copying. In the United Kingdom such
licences are issued by the Copyright Licensing Agency, 90
Tottenham Court Road, London, W1P 9HE. The right of Neville
Turner to be identified as the author of this work has been asserted
by him in accordance with Copyright Designs and Patents Act
1988.

To my dear wife, Chris.
"The wind beneath my wings"

Contents

THANKS TO

Bill Mitchell, a source of encour-
agement and friendship for many
years.

Everyone at the Dalesman
Publishing Company for their
faith in my work.

Eddie Straiton for his support and
enthusiasm

All my friends in the Dales. The
expansion of my knowledge of any
topic in this book was never more
than a phone call away.

This ewe and thousands more like her play a critical part in the economy of the Pennine hill farmer. She is the product of a Swaledale ewe crossed with a Leicester tup. Buyers from all over the country value her conformation (physical traits) and mothering qualities. Crossed with a heavy breed, her progeny will have fine carcass quality.

Foreword by Robert Hardy CBE, FSA

I write this foreword with the repellent, acrid stench of animal pyres blowing across Britain, as thousands upon thousands of both infected and healthy stock, slaughtered in the Foot and Mouth debacle, are incinerated. I hope that by the time this splendid volume reaches the reader the worst of the blight may have passed. What this mishandled crisis has cruelly underlined is the shocking lack of comprehension, on the part of urban government and the great urban majority, of the life and world of farming and the country. What this book achieves is to bring into sharp focus, in the simply written word and the author's own marvellously evocative pictures, the lives of one large and scattered group of farmer-shepherds in the Pennine hills and dales.

Having pretended to be a vet in the Dales for some years, I feel I recognise every skyline, field and fieldhouse in these pages; pages in which Neville Turner lays before us the beauty, the challenges and harsh demands that come with the changing seasons and indeed with the changing climate, for hill farmers and their partner vets; his pictures truly catch those seasons under the fickle northern skies. Most happily we share in his moments of triumph and in the slow, steady achievements of the farmers whose friendship he has earned and to whom he has given such long, unfailing service.

Introduction

Opposite. In the winter months fog can roll down the little valleys like a tidal wave or an avalanche. As it hits you the temperature drops in an instant and the air takes on a clammy feel. The bare branches of the trees which a few moments before starkly contrasted against the bright sky become wisps of darker grey in a grey world.

But take the road up the hill. As you emerge from beneath the shroud, the sun and bright sky are still there and the hilltops have become islands in a vast white sea.

In the months leading up to my retirement, I had made it quite clear that there was to be no fuss, no parties and no speeches. Chris, my wife, was surreptitiously approached with a view to arranging surprise "dos", but parried these suggestions in accordance with my wishes. A few weeks into retirement I thought that we had succeeded in bowing out discreetly, but it was not to be. The hill farmers, the families farming near or above the 1000ft mark, had not taken "no" for an answer. They had all dug deep into their pockets and subscribed, in these hard times for farming, to lay on a splendid supper and presentation in a small hotel at the top of the dale.

It was a memorable evening. The formalities were short, thank goodness. The inevitable lump in my throat and the dewy eyes (my main reasons for wishing to avoid such an occasion) were never far away. I managed to have a chat with everyone present, and lost count of the times I was asked, "Do you remember the first time you came to our farm?" In most cases I was able to recall first meetings in detail, and many of the subsequent ones too. For over a quarter of a century I had been in daily contact with these folk. A mutual respect and trust had been forged. A lucky man, I had spent my working life travelling in some of the most beautiful countryside in the British Isles, in a job which on a good day was like earning one's living by visiting friends.

The hill farmer is a remarkable character, with a resilience, capacity for hard work and sense of humour that I have always admired. In this narrative I shall be referring to "he" and "him" when speaking of the hill farmer. This is purely for convenience and it in no way suggests a disregard of the distaff. Wives' and offsprings' input of effort and commitment are in most cases as important as that of the man of the family. Occasionally, and for a variety of reasons, there may not be an adult male involved in the running of the farm. A famous case in point was Hannah Hauxwell, who ploughed a lonely furrow in Baldersdale.

The hill farmer has a tradition going back three and a half thousand

This old Swaledale ewe has a fine lamb sired by a Leicester tup. She spent her first three or four breeding seasons producing pure-bred sons and daughters in the high Pennines, but her latter alliances will be "down-country" and will result in cross bred lambs. As spring turns to summer and buttercups bespeckle the fields it can be seen that the lamb has grown rapidly since its arrival at Easter.

years to when the very first recognisable farms appeared in the man-made clearings in the vast forest that covered the hills. Progress occurred only slowly. Fifteen hundred years later farms had become a little more numerous on the Pennine hills; the only major changes were that the descendants of the bronze age pioneers had cleared most of the upland of trees, learned to smelt iron and refined their cereal technology. There is some tenuous evidence that the coming of the Romans in about AD70 through to their departure three hundred years or so later was a period of economic boom for the hill farmer. It is suggested that the Romans never completely dominated the dalesmen, who capitalised on the fact that large armies need supplies. Our Romano-British hill farmer could provide horses, meat, corn, hides, tallow, wool and timber.

Farming practices were not significantly altered by either the Anglo-Saxons or the Vikings. The latter did not come as marauding plunderers as is commonly imagined, but mainly as settlers spreading back east-wards from Norse colonies in Ireland and the Lake District. Scandinavian place names and farming terms survive to this day.

The first three centuries of the second millennium were not good for the hill farmer in the Pennines. Scots armies wrought havoc from the border to south Yorkshire well into the fourteenth century. The poor farmer took a simultaneous pasting from the south as well, for William the Conqueror, less than pleased with resistance to his conquest, "laid waste" vast areas north of the Humber between 1072 and 1086. "Laying waste" meant just that. People and stock were put to the sword, farms were burnt to the ground and ploughs were destroyed.

The life of the hill farmer under the rule of the Norman lords was diffi-cult. As well as scratching a living from the thin soils of the dales, the peasant farmer had to pay dues in the form of goods or services. The Norman lords, mindful of their spiritual welfare, were generous to the church in the form of land and grazing rights. Dues then became payable to the Bishop instead of the feudal lord. Between 1130 and 1300, the Bali-ols granted various charters to the monastic husbandrymen of Rievaulx Abbey allowing them to graze their animals in various locations in Tees-dale. In one year the charter records their stock in the dale as 270 mares, 18 stallions, 114 cows, 9 bulls, 6 oxen and 340 sheep.

The dues to the Bishop of Durham for the village of Stanhope in upper

Weardale in 1183 illustrate how onerous these duties were.

"In Stanhope there are 20 villeins each of whom holds one bovate and pays two shillings, and works for 16 days with one man between Pentecost and the feast of St Martin in winter, and carts corn for four days with one cart, and does four obligatory days, and mows the meadows for two days, and prepares and leads the hay, and he carries loads and does riding duties between Stanhope and Wolsingham, and carries venison to Durham. Moreover all the villeins build a kitchen, and a larder and a dog kennel at the Great Chases and they provide straw for the hall, chapel, and chamber and they lead all the Bishop's supplies from Wolsingham to the lodges."

Between the Norman and Tudor periods, small villages appeared, and there was a trend to enclose fields. The drystone wall replaced banks of earth and boulders which had previously been used. Wall building proliferated and with it came improvements in agriculture which were to continue with accelerating pace to the present day. The Enclosure Acts between 1780 and 1840 resulted in the hundreds of miles of long, straight stone walls which now form the most significant man-made feature in our dales landscape (apart from the heather moors which have been created and maintained by steady grazing). The nineteenth century was unique in that there was a dual economy. Family members working in the flourishing lead mining industry supplemented farm incomes.

And then our hill farmer faced the twentieth century.

If we disregard the economic slump in the Thirties, the first half of the twentieth century was probably the best in the whole of his three and a half thousand year history. New breeds of cattle and sheep enabled production from farms to reach new highs. Productivity was encouraged and nurtured by the needs of two major wars. Mechanisation, the likes of which had never been seen before, relieved the hill farmer of hours of hard manual toil.

And then it hit him. Global economics and politics crept onto the scene, slowly at first, but with increasing power and significance. The hill farmer had successfully faced change and challenges throughout his history, but never such swingeing changes nor such daunting challenges. The unrelenting pressures forced him into an unenviable posi-

I love being "Hon. Vet" at the local agricultural show, although it's a busy day. Between midday and 1pm I squeeze in a convivial lunch and a tour of the marquees then change into uniform to do my bit in the cornet section of the village band for a two-hour ringside concert. If the officials need my services during this period, they know exactly where to find me.

This dual role had an amusing consequence a few years ago when I was summoned from the bandstand to attend a dog with a damaged leg. The owners were a dear couple who were very grateful for my prompt service but bemused at the vet turning up in green jacket with black facings, lots of gold braid and a black bow tie! The story found its way into the *Northern Echo* the

following week in a superbly witty tongue-in-cheek piece, the gist of which was that the show must be a very high-class affair when the "Hon. Vet" turns up in full livery.

The ringside concert comes to a close at 3pm in time for the grand parade of prizewinners. Almost before the parade has cleared the arena, the sulky racers are on the track, hurtling around at amazing speeds on what appears to be little more than a pair of shafts and bicycle wheels. The races, fifteen or more, are all frantic, making the great chariot race from *Ben Hur* look like kids' stuff.

I feel that at any moment I may have to sort out a major catastrophe. The "Hon. Medical Officer" must feel the same. However, whilst the drivers are

keen, daring and immensely competitive, they are also very skilful and major mishaps seldom occur.

Left. It's a dull and very cold winter's day in the hills. The sheep are more than ready for a dose of summer sunshine preserved in their daily hay ration. Contrary to popular belief, sheep do have some brainpower. They knew what time it was. The scene was like something from a Fifties' cowboys and Indians' film. They had assembled on the highest ground to lie in wait for the wagon train and now it's arrived they tear down the hillside to attack the "chuck wagon".

Right. I have seen the breathtaking beauty of the "fall" in the American Mid-West: it is a riot of incredible colours that blanket hundreds of square miles of the landscape.

Autumn in the Pennines is, shall we say, different. We do not have the vast numbers of mature trees. We do not have the huge variety of species. Violent wintry winds can be quick on the heels of a fading summer, stripping away every leaf overnight. However, this birch tree is being allowed to make its subtle changes from green through pale yellows to pure gold.

Birch copses are a delightful feature of the dales. One of my favourites is truly ancient woodland, haunt of woodcock and roe deer. It has a mystical quality. In May a wall-to-wall carpet of bluebells enhances its beauty. And when autumn is kind, it puts on its own little display of breathtaking "fall" colours.

HILL FARMER

tion. He had to "run faster just to stand still". Increasing efficiency and enhancing productivity became necessary to maintain a level income. Mechanisation and the quest for such efficiency rendered thousands of agricultural workers redundant. They all left the fields to find employment in more stable industries. The life of the hill farmer was becoming not only more demanding, but also more isolated. He and his family were alone in this race that no one could win.

It was in the Fifties and Sixties that the drive for production contributed to the popularity of artificial insemination in the dairy cow, pushing up production by using sires from families with phenomenal milking records. At the same time the beef industry started to use bulls of the large, rapidly-maturing, Continental breeds. The traditional British breeds, which were designed to thrive on the hill pastures, were abandoned. Thus increasing demands were being made on the stock as well as on the farmer, but it was still possible that by running faster he could continue to maintain a reasonable living. Then it all went awry. In the Eighties BSE struck. Its effects were devastating. Export markets disappeared overnight. New regulations and restrictions put incredible stresses on the hill farmer. The beef industry was in crisis, and shortly after that, for various economic and political reasons, the sheep trade hit crisis too. Stress assailed the hill farmer from all sides.

Sue Shaw, the former project manager with an agricultural support group, did extensive research on the problems that have beset the hill farmer. In her year 2000 update on this research, she outlines the current stress factors. "The strength of sterling against the 'euro', in which farm subsidies are measured, declining commodity prices, changes in the European Common Agricultural Policy, increasing bureaucracy, continual change in grant schemes, the increasingly complex system of animal passports resulting from the BSE crisis, and the subsequent concerns over food safety, have all added to the existing cocktail of stressors acting upon the farmers. In addition, the agricultural workforce is ageing and many farm businesses do not have a successor.

"Paperwork, financial concerns and the post-BSE situation are still the farmer's three major worries, added to which are the isolation factor, the public's view of farming and the government's attitude to the countryside."

Opposite above. The hill farmer enjoying a day's rough shooting with a few friends, every one a countryman with a deep respect for, and knowledge of, his quarry. The quality of the sport is exceeded only by the quality of the company. A hundred tales of shooting are exchanged during the course of the day.

In the evening, they'll have supper together round a table groaning with home-made fare, and tell a few more good stories.

Opposite below. The Border Collie. He has the speed and stamina of an athlete, a devotion to his master and an eagerness to obey. There is alertness to rapidly changing situations: the eye monitors the picture; the ear constantly listens for signals. Reaction times to these stimuli are like lightning. The capacity for work is incredible. Most would run to the point of exhaustion if allowed.

Breeding dogs to physical criteria is difficult enough, but to recognise and breed towards inherited behavioural traits at the same time is a phenomenal undertaking. The crouch, the eye, the keenness and intelligence are all inherited separately.

I was told of a reporter from a local newspaper who had interviewed a hill farmer who'd hit the jackpot on the national lottery. When asked if the millions of pounds would change his life and if he would be giving up farming, the farmer replied: "Nay lad, I'll just carry on farming till it's all gone." The story may be apocryphal, and you may have heard it before, but the significant point is that it was told to me by a hill farmer with a wry smile on his face. In the depths of this economic depression he was still able to smile. He was still able to be philosophical. The hill farmer, like the red grouse, will stay welded to these moors. He will remain realistic and adopt any changes that may be necessary in order to survive.

The strategy for survival has been strangely similar to the one used by the hill farmers of two hundred years ago, when meagre incomes were supplemented by a source from outside agriculture. At that time it was lead mining and walling. Today the repertoire is far more diverse. Many wives have made use of professional qualifications and gone back to careers. The farmer himself may have taken part-time employment while still running the farm. Capitalising on skills such as photography and craftwork can generate extra income. In some cases this diversification has been directed within agriculture, as in the direct selling of home-produced quality beef and lamb at farmers' markets.

For many, opportunities are presented by the flourishing tourist industry. Some find jobs in hotels, restaurants and tourist information centres. Others have opted for direct involvement by offering farmhouse bed and breakfast or full farmhouse holidays. A co-operative of farmers involved in the tourist industry promotes a "Stay on a Farm" scheme. In some cases redundant farm buildings have been tastefully converted into holiday cottages. The hill farmer and his family have not just bemoaned their lot. They have taken the necessary steps to negotiate these difficult times. They have shown amazing character, talent and ingenuity.

The "running faster to stand still" syndrome over the last few decades was caused by financial pressures on all farmers to keep more and more stock and to embrace the philosophy of intensive farming. Subsidies were, in the main, based on "headage", the numbers of stock being kept. Productivity-wise that seemed to make sense, but it was a never-ending upward spiral. It was indeed a race that no one could win. It had to lead to over-stocking and over-grazing. At last I see signs from Brussels and Westminster that they acknowledge the folly of such a philosophy and are making moves which must be to the benefit of the hill farmer.

In 2001, a new Hill Farm Allowance is due to be introduced. It will be based on the area of the farm rather than the numbers of stock kept there. This has to be good news. A new Countryside Stewardship Scheme and a rigorous Extensification Scheme are to be announced. Cynics might see this as a subsidy to turn the hill farmer into a custodian of an enormous park. I see it as an opportunity for the hill farmer to do what he excels at, namely, turning out a top-quality product using extensive, sustainable techniques. In doing so farming will be at one with the environment. The heather moors, flower-rich meadows, and patchwork of walled fields will be preserved, not as a museum piece, but as a shining example of how productive agriculture need not be at variance with a sensitivity for the landscape, ecology and heritage.

An added bonus in this scenario is that the social structure of the dales will not be destroyed. The drift of population away from the rural environment will be halted. The village brass bands, agricultural shows, caring communities and way of life will endure. The hill farmer will be acknowledged for the vital part he plays in British agriculture.

This book is a document recording some aspects of farming, its environment and its associated culture in the dales. It illustrates how a mastery of the old skills of stockmanship, a grasp of modern technologies and a constant battle against the harsh climate are necessary to survive. My position of trust has not been abused. My camera has merely been a third eye, a fly on the wall in the everyday chores and dramas in the life of my friend: the hill farmer.

Spring

A spectacular view of the heatherburn. Shepherds and keepers have been managing the high hills of the dales like this for centuries. If it were left unchecked, heather would grow high and woody. There would be little food value in it for sheep or grouse.

At first sight it looks as though nothing could survive this treatment, but the operator's skill, experience and knowledge of the terrain, will ensure that the result has long-term benefits. The ground needs to be wet and the whole of the heather plant needs to be dry. The aim is to burn off all of the plant that lies above the surface. Regeneration is swift. There are vast amounts of heather seed in the upper layers of moorland ground but these will stay dormant unless exposed to direct light. Removing the canopy of rank heather admits the light and stimulates fresh germination. In the perfect burn with swift removal of old vegetation and minimal scorching of the ground, new life may also spring from basal buds of unharmed rootstock. Growth from these basal buds is strong and rapid since they already have functional roots in place.

And the spring comes slowly up this way.

The words of Coleridge ring true for the hill farmer. The first signs of spring are the flocks of peewits returning to the hills to breed in mid-February, but they, like their host the hill farmer, are optimists. Often a late snowstorm in April will produce the sad sight of these birds sitting on nests on the pasture with only their heads visible above a six-inch blanket of snow. The hill farmer knows that spring can be the briefest of interludes between the bad weather and a short summer.

The winter routine of foddering cattle begins in November and extends into mid-May. The hill farmer dares not think about lambing his sheep until April. Even then a newly born lamb may be frozen to the ground after a hard frost. He regularly sees his ewes and lambs huddled in the lee of a drystone wall taking shelter from horizontal sleet.

More than twenty years ago in the TV documentary which brought fame to Hannah Hauxwell, much of the footage was devoted to the Bainbridges of Birkdale and their love of the beauty and character of the high Pennines. Brian Bainbridge pointed out the main disadvantage of living there. It was taken up and used for the title of the documentary.

It was called *Too Long A Winter*.

Heather burning

These dense plumes of smoke seldom occur singly. If the weather is right for heather burning, it's odds-on that all the keepers in the area will seize the opportunity. Although the permitted season for heather burning runs from the beginning of October through to mid-April there may be only a few days when conditions are just right. In the autumn the ground is generally too dry. To start a fire in such conditions carries serious risk of igniting the peat: the consequences would be disastrous. Everything is either too wet or covered in snow during the winter months so there is always a flurry of activity in the last six to eight weeks before burning becomes illegal. There is some urgency to complete the programme since in a sound management plan most of the moor will be burned in a ten to fifteen year cycle.

The heat generated by a vigorous heatherburn is intense. It is not uncommon for a less than cautious operator to return home with a blistered face and singed clothing.

Heather seed is a remarkable plant form to withstand such a blast and then burst into life after many years in the dormant state. Indeed, botanists investigating its properties found that a "toasting" actually helped to promote successful germination. Another interesting find was that although the burn and exposure to light act as a trigger, not all such stimulated seeds will germinate in year one. Some will spring to life two or three years later. Thus if the weather in year one is not favourable for germination, it is not a problem. A second and third wave of seeds will follow in subsequent years.

Control of a heatherburn is essential. The operator will have considered many factors before starting the fire. How wet is the ground? How dry is the heather? An uphill burn or downhill? What is the wind strength and direction?

Strangely enough it is probably easier to keep control of a fire lit in a strong wind than in a light one. A strong wind tends to maintain its direction so it is easy to predict the path of the burn. A lighter wind can veer so that it is impossible to control the burn's path.

Dosing sheep

Hill sheep graze vast areas of the heather moorland but occasionally there is a need to gather the flock into a place where they can be handled. To achieve this shepherds have always constructed folds or pens at strategic points. Originally the sheepfolds were simple enclosures surrounded by high drystone walls. These pens were almost always circular to avoid crushing and suffocation in corners. This is the modern version.

A cleverly designed network of interconnecting pens, gates, alleyways and races facilitates quick and efficient handling. Sheep from one part of the moor can be kept separate from sheep from another part, and at the end of the operation returned to their own "heaf". The concrete base ensures clean working conditions and provides a strong footing for the retaining fences.

The sheep are being given medication to prevent disease caused by liver fluke. The medication is given by mouth. A measured dose is dispensed by means of a dosing gun, which is automatically replenished from a pack on the shepherd's back. With the sheep restrained in the narrow race the process is stress free for both the operator and the patient.

Gathering sheep from the fell into such pens was, until relatively recently, a long and arduous day's work.

It entailed miles of walking over difficult ground. Three men on quad bikes and a good team of dogs gathered these sheep in an incredibly short time.

Pregnancy scanning in sheep

It doesn't seem long since ultrasound scanning of the foetus "in utero" was a remarkable innovation in human health care. It says much for the hill farmer's readiness to grasp modern technology that he very quickly realised that the procedure could be of value to him in his flock management.

The sheep have been gathered into a convenient building and a race constructed. Everything must be ready in good time. Adrian has set up his equipment and from his low seat can run his probe across the sheep's abdomen. As soon as a good image appears on the screen he will announce his opinion on the pregnancy, flick a lever to release the sheep, and ready himself to engage the head restraint on his next subject. The speed at which he can work is phenomenal.

Sheep are scanned at about the 90th day of their 150 day pregnancy. The image on Adrian's screen will not only differentiate the pregnant and non-pregnant sheep, but will also tell him how many lambs are present in each pregnancy. The farmer stands by with a selection of coloured marking aerosols to record this information on each sheep.

Later they will be sorted into groups. The barren ewes and those carrying only one lamb will need no special treatment, but the feeding and management of those with twins and triplets will be suitably adjusted.

Scanning is carried out by a highly skilled operator. Since the season is short he must work long hours and be very quick. He carries a specially designed handling crate and all the technical equipment in his vehicle but relies on an efficient, well-manned system to run the sheep through a race and hence into the restraint. Neighbours or family need to turn out to ensure a steady flow of stock through the system. Here a young man does his bit to ensure rapid presentation of his father's sheep.

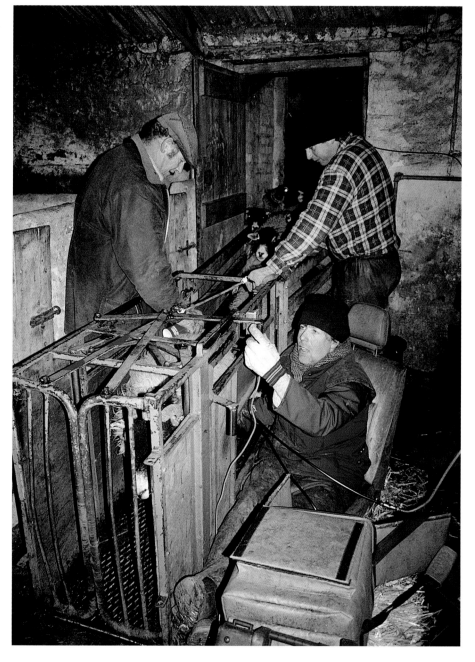

Lambing

The Swaledale is the favoured breed of the hill farmer. The Rough Fell and the Dalesbred occur in smaller numbers. Here we see a Jacob's sheep, a slightly unusual sight, but not uncommon in the lower dales. She has a fine set of triplets. Whatever the breed, it's pretty tough being a lamb, and the problems start even before you're born.

If mum hasn't succumbed to any one of half a dozen infectious diseases that result in abortion or stillbirth, she could yet be affected by metabolic disorders such as "staggers" or "twin lamb disease". The former is a rapidly fatal drop in blood calcium, but prompt treatment by the shepherd will avert disaster. The latter is an insidious form of pregnancy toxaemia. Treatment does not enjoy spectacular success.

Low copper levels in the ewe's blood during pregnancy will lead to abnormality in the development of the lamb's brain and an incurable spastic condition called "swayback" in the lamb.

Having survived the hazards of pregnancy, mother and offspring are faced with surviving the ordeal of the actual birth process where all sorts of things can go wrong. And so the lamb is born, but that's not the end of the story. Some ewes at this stage get fed up with the whole business and reject the lamb. Others are very motherly but fail to produce milk for the first twenty-four to forty-eight hours.

The lamb's wet navel immediately after birth is an excellent medium for the entry of all manner of germs which can cause peritonitis, liver abscesses and septic arthritis. Bowel infections leading to acute and fatal diarrhoea are a danger. Apart from infections, serious losses occur from hypothermia, mismothering and starvation.

Happy bands of lambs skipping about in the spring sunshine don't just happen. The skilled and dedicated flockmaster makes it happen.

Often, when called to a lambing, the vet attends to the patient in the middle of a field. As long as you can drive your car to a spot nearby so that all your equipment is on hand, and a bucket of clean, warm water, soap and towel are available, it's not a problem. It's probably less stressful to the expectant mother too.

That was the case with this pedigree Leicester ewe. Her difficulty was a common one: failure of the cervix to open up and let the lambs through. Most times, gentle manipulation and lots of lubrication will solve the problem. However, in this ewe no progress had been made after twenty minutes of trying, so the only solution was a Caesarean operation. The weather was good and all the equipment was to hand so the field became my operating table.

As the operation is performed under local anaesthesia she was able to rise to her feet immediately, no worse for her experience, and enjoy acquainting herself with her three fine lambs.

About three months later, I was back at the farm attending to a routine call. When I'd finished the job, the farmer was anxious to show me the results of our efforts in the lambing field. I was delighted to oblige and see the results of the surgery "al fresco". Mum had raised two of her lambs, whilst the third had been fostered onto a Swaledale ewe. The lambs had done well, and I thought it a great opportunity for a picture.

Stage-managing an animal for a portrait requires time and patience. Stage-managing four at the same time is nigh impossible. It took me longer to set this one up than it took to do the operation three months before!

Veterinary students gain their practical knowledge of lambing time by taking jobs as assistant shepherds during their Easter holidays. I spent one "spring" in horizontal Pennine sleet, and another in the late snows of the Cheviots. The knowledge thus gained is coupled with the academic input of term time, to produce skills that will help the farmer to solve apparently insoluble delivery problems.

I loved the challenge of a lambing case. Shepherds are skilled midwives and when they run out of ideas, the lambing isn't going to be easy. Patience, gentleness, a logical approach and copious quantities of obstetric lubricant are the key to success. Each breed has its own particular difficulties. In the Swaledale it can be the precocious horn growth of the tup lambs. In the Texel it's the lamb's broad bony forehead. Here, in the Leicester, the lambs have long limbs and necks which can perform the most amazing contortions, and three lambs performing contortions in the confined space of the uterus can be fun to disentangle.

I'd left my bed at 2am to sort this one out. It was a challenge but it was a success. Three warm, wet, leggy little bodies lay in the straw, steam rising from them in the chilly early morning air. The dam's reassuring motherly grunts answered their bleating.

Horn burning

The hill farmer's sheep flock spends much of its time on the open moor, which is unfenced. I suppose that in theory a hill sheep could do the Pennine Way from Derbyshire to the Scottish Borders if it so desired. (Although the M62 trans-Pennine motorway could be a bit of a problem.) The reason they do not go in for long distance walking is that most are "heafed" or "hefted" which means that each flock knows and sticks to its own patch of moorland. There are a few wanderers so owner-identification is important. This is achieved by various combinations of hornburns, paint brands and ear markings.

Paint brands can fade and ear tags can be lost but a hornburn endures and would be very difficult to alter. It is achieved by heating branding irons in a brazier and impressing these into the horn. The procedure is totally painless for the sheep but looks awfully uncomfortable for the operator. Each farm has its own individual brand which usually stays with that farm even when ownership changes.

The brand usually takes the form of letters and is always applied in a specific pattern, either to the right or left horn, or occasionally to both.

The fresh hornburn. All the horn, ear and fleece marks are registered in *The Shepherd's Guide*, a remarkable publication that covers the 1600 or so hill farmers who graze sheep on the moors of the northern Pennines. It also ordains the time and place where stray sheep can be collected or returned to their rightful owners. The list of meeting places is extensive but is intelligently devised into geographic areas. Here is an illustration from an old edition:

"At Nateby near Kirkby Stephen; Hardrow in Wensleydale; Unicorn Inn, Bowes; and CB Inn, Arkengarthdale on the first Monday after the 8th of July for the Midsummer; and on the first Monday after the 3rd of November for the autumn gathering."

Collies

The modern Border Collie is a much loved friend and an indispensable part of the team on any livestock farm. No better description has ever been written than that penned by Robert Burns in his *Twa Dogs*

He was a gash and faithful tyke
As ever lap a sheugh or dyke
His honest, sonsie, baws'nt face
Made him friends in ilka place.
His breast was white, his touzie back
Weel clad wi' coat o' glossy black
His gaucie tail wi' upward curl
Hung ower his hurdies wi' a swirl

Collie dogs like to know what's going on. They'll inspect each new arrival in the farmyard. To do so a bit of DIY may be necessary – like removing a piece of door. I know one who can drive a hole straight through the middle!

In his *Modern Farriery* published in 1820, Lawson describes two types of shepherd's dog. His description of the Cur dog leads me to suspect that this is the forerunner of the Border Collie. In many places the breed is still referred to as a Cur dog.

Lawson states, "This useful animal in the north is called the Coally Dog. They are chiefly employed in driving cattle. They are stronger and fiercer than the shepherd's dog and the hair is smoother and shorter. They are mostly of the black and white colour. Their ears are half pricked. Their sagacity is uncommonly great."

In the hundreds of farmyards I visited I was always intrigued by the variety of accommodation provided for the sheepdogs. I've seen the traditional gabled design executed in wood, aluminium, and corrugated sheeting. Redundant water tanks are commonly used. And there are, of course, the home-designed-cobbled-together-from-bits-of-wood variety. One elegant home is fashioned from a large oak-staved barrel.

This home is what the estate agents would call a "desirable residence" and very much in keeping with the local architecture.

As long as they're waterproof, draught-proof and well bedded it really doesn't matter what they look like.

The picture suggests that he's into long distance walking! Some collies are quite happy wandering loose in the farmyard but others need to be tethered. I've had some heart-stopping moments emerging from my car to find a Hound of the Baskervilles coming at me with teeth bared. The relief of realising that he's attached by a chain to his kennel gives way to panic when one realises that it's an awfully long chain!

Sheepdog trials

In his book, *One Man and his Dog*, Phil Drabble tells of the amazing success of the TV programme of the same name. It's a fascinating story with a most unlikely beginning. An imaginative TV producer, Philip Gilbert, on holiday in Northumberland, happened to spend a day at a local agricultural show. One of the fringe activities that caught his eye was a sheepdog trial. In spite of the pouring rain, he watched, intrigued by the spectacle. From the germ of an idea planted in Philip's mind that day sprang the TV series of legendary success.

Viewing figures of one million would have been considered excellent, but the very first series attracted *two* million. At the height of its popularity six million watched, and there was uproar when the programme was "axed".

Here we have one man and his dog at a nursery trial near Leyburn. I love watching the scene at the starting post. The dog is so keen, bursting with enthusiasm to get on with it, but won't move a whisker until the boss says so.

Over a hundred years ago, working shepherds, with little formal education and still less knowledge of the science of genetics, applied their wisdom and expertise to perform wonders of genetic engineering. We're not talking genetic engineering in a test tube. We're talking of painstakingly mixing and matching a host of complex behavioural traits which come together to give the Border Collie its superb herding ability.

Here we see the most mystical of his qualities, the "eye". It is indeed a mystical quality, for it is nothing but a freezing of posture and a hypnotic stare. We see exactly the same phenomenon in the pointers and setters, so it comes as no surprise that there is a suggestion of this gun-dog blood in the collie. Some collies even raise the foreleg, pointer-style, as they freeze.

The shepherd not only recognises this quality, but also can assess the strength of the quality. If the "eye" is too strong the dog becomes transfixed, oblivious to all other senses, including his master's commands. If the "eye" is too weak, the magical hypnotic control of the sheep will be lost.

One Man and his Dog was a superbly chosen title, for it sums up the fascination of sheepdog work. The bond, the communication, the whistles and the signals mark a unique co-operation in getting the job done. Thanks to the programme, many folk who have never been to a trial are familiar with the technical terms such as "outrun", "lift", "cross-drive", "shedding" and "penning". It is only in the latter two manoeuvres where there is any physical co-operation between the two parties, and penning shows off this co-operation admirably.

At the appropriate point in the trial, the shepherd makes his way to the pen made from hurdles. One of the hurdles can swing, and forms the gate to the pen. At the free end of the gate, a six-foot rope is attached. The shepherd grasps the end of the rope and is thus able to control the opening and closing of the gate. He is not allowed to release his grip on the rope until the sheep are in the pen. For me this is the most exciting part of the trial. If one sheep makes a break, or if the dog makes a hasty move, the delicate operation can go awry.

Mole-catching

It may not be immediately obvious why the hill farmer and the mole don't get along. Yes, the pastures do become disfigured when there are too many molehills, but the mole's lifestyle creates more serious problems. As well as destroying the sward and making life difficult for machinery, molehills are responsible for causing stock to ingest more soil than is good for them.

This soil intake can disrupt the digestive processes of ruminants, precipitate mineral deficiencies, and transmit Listeriosis which is an infection causing meningitis and abortion.

As winter eases its grip on the dales, the whole landscape erupts with mole activity. The first three months of the year, before the grass hides the damage, are also months of frantic activity for the mole catcher.

The trap is sprung. Each trap is marked with a small flag so that the mole catcher can do his rounds quickly and efficiently. As an extra precaution against losing traps he will also have drawn a sketch map of the field and plotted the site of each trap when it was laid the previous day. The traps are expensive but they are also humane.

Mole-catching is an art. It is full of mysticism and secrets. A good mole catcher can clear a field in one sweep of diligent trap-laying. A brief look at the field is enough for the trapper to familiarise himself with the pattern of mole activity. A metal rod probes the ground to locate the tunnel. A spade will remove a small square of turf to expose the run and the trap is laid.

Bulleting cattle

Many hill pastures are deficient in certain trace elements that are necessary for the health of the grazing animal. The commonest of these deficiencies are copper, cobalt and selenium. Lack of one or more of the three can cause a variety of problems. There may be infertility in the breeding stock or poor growth rates in the young along with other symptoms. A blood sample is usually taken to find a diagnosis.

As with most diseases prevention is better than cure, and a farm with a history of deficiency disease will generally ensure that stock are supplemented before "turn out" in the spring.

The simplest way to achieve this is to administer a large bolus or "bullet" by mouth. This will dissolve slowly in the rumen ensuring a steady supply of the required elements.

Although this may be the simplest solution to the problem of deficiency disease, it is not necessarily the easiest to carry out! A good cattle crush with an efficient head restraint is necessary along with a dosing gun designed to take one or two large boluses.

The operator needs to be firm, gentle and very patient.

The loaded dosing gun is directed carefully over the back of the tongue, avoiding the large and powerful molar teeth; a trigger on the gun is then used to release the bolus. The bolus must be swallowed intact if it is to lie in the rumen and do its job properly.

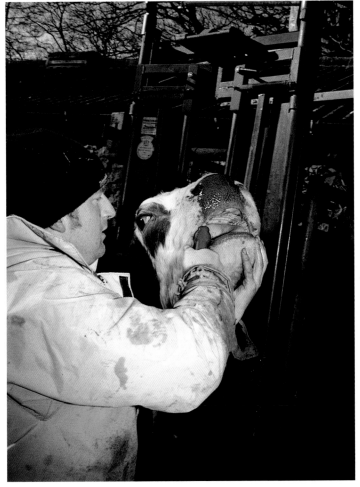

Calving

I've always marvelled at the miracle of birth. The instincts which nature has put in place ensure that most cows and ewes can handle it quite nicely without any human interference. It's wonderful to watch a normal delivery, the way that the dam licks and nudges the new arrival to dry it and stimulate it: the way the calf or lamb knows where the udder is and what it's for. Nature has arranged that those first few sucks will provide energy, vitamins and protection from disease.

But the stockman keeps a close watch on any cow in labour. He senses when something is amiss and investigates the problem. Often he can assist competently but if things appear complicated, then it's time to call the vet.

I loved the dash to a calving case, the excitement of not knowing what the problem would be until I had made my first examination, and the challenge of sorting it out.

In a normal delivery the calf appears with its forelimbs first and the head tucked snugly between them. Unless the calf is particularly big, such a delivery needs no assistance at all. Things become complicated when there is a departure from the norm.

In this case the calf was presented backwards, not a major problem if the feet are coming first, but Richard felt only a tail. The calf's hind legs extended forwards so that the hind feet lay somewhere near the calf's ears. This is a true "breech" presentation. To effect delivery the feet must be located and brought into the birth canal without damaging the uterus.

Having corrected the presentation, ropes are attached to the calf's legs. In the old days the traction was applied by as many strong men as could be mustered, but nowadays the mechanical device takes some of the sweat out of it.

Meadows

In April the glossy foliage and buds of
the Marsh Marigold, (*Caltha palustris*)
cover the marshy upland meadows. At
the first hint of real warmth from the
sun in May the buds open in synchrony
and the landscape is transformed
overnight to a golden-yellow carpet as
far as the eye can see.

William Fothergill wrote of dales farming in 1794: "…and the meadows, which are all natural, abound with herbs which, being more succulent than the grasses, are more difficult to harvest."

Caesarean section in cattle

Long before this technique appeared in the standard veterinary textbooks Eddie Straiton, a hard working country vet and one of the profession's most colourful characters, worked out how this operation could be done. Eddie was later to be awarded the OBE and achieved worldwide fame as the "TV vet". Using a great deal of common sense and no small measure of courage, he pioneered the technique that is now in the routine repertoire of all farm animal practitioners.

For practical reasons the operation is best carried out with the animal fully conscious and in the standing position. This is achieved by local anaesthesia of the whole of the left flank. Although I have performed hundreds of these operations, I'm still bemused at the fact that major surgery is performed with the animal blissfully unaware of what is going on.

Often one of the most difficult aspects of the "Caesar" is deciding whether or not the operation is necessary. Is a successful delivery possible, or will the calf stick halfway? Here, the veterinary surgeon, Jenny, adjusts the presentation of the calf, attaches ropes to feet and head, and directs gentle traction. As the calf engages in the cow's pelvis, it becomes obvious that a normal delivery is impossible. Too much traction would precipitate a point of no return, so as soon as the decision is made, the ropes are removed and preparations for surgery begin.

At busy times the vet will recruit assistance from the farmer or his family. If possible, as in this case, it's wonderful to have the luxury of a second vet present. The cow's left flank has been clipped, shaved, and scrubbed with antiseptic. Although conditions in a cattle building may appear less than satisfactory, a strict adherence to sterile technique ensures that post-operative infection is rare. Jenny can be seen opening a pack of sterile instruments. At this stage local anaesthesia will be complete and the whole of the cow's left flank will be devoid of sensation. Preparation for surgery actually takes much more time than the delivery of the calf.

24 hours post-surgery. Mother and son are both doing well. The cow is usually prescribed a course of antibiotics to reduce the risk of infection. Apart from that there is no special aftercare. Whilst the internal stitches are catgut and will dissolve, the skin sutures are nylon and will need to be removed in ten to fourteen days.

Most cows will breed normally the following year. Occasionally I have performed the operation on cows which have had a Caesarean section a year or two before and have been surprised to find no evidence of any scar tissue or previous interference.

Muck-spreading

Fieldhouse, byre, or large new building – all have one thing in common: an ever-increasing mountain of manure accumulates outside over the long winter months. This must be spread on the meadows before the grass starts to grow.

In the old days before mechanisation this was quite an arduous task. A low cart or sledge would be loaded with the manure and taken out into the field. The cart would be stopped at regular intervals to offload part of its contents. There would be dozens of heaps in a single field. Then the really hard work began. Using a gripe the farmer had to spread or "scale" each pile so that it was evenly distributed across the field. Finally horse-drawn chain harrows were used to spread the manure more evenly.

Often this work was contracted out to casual labour and, strangely enough, this still tends to be the case today, although the labour is anything but "casual". Specialist contractors with up-to-date equipment are appointed to the task.

The problem, which causes a race against time in getting the job done, is the weather. The dales meadows in late winter and early spring tend to be very wet. Heavy machinery would carve up the sward and may even become bogged down. Sharp frosts are a bonus, for that puts a hard crust on the fields and the work can proceed.

The muck-spreading contractor will often have, as well as the muck-spreader, machinery to transfer the manure to the spreader. Here he is using a skid-steer. A few grabs from the muck heap will fill the muck-spreader in minutes.

The skid-steer is an amazing machine. A range of interchangeable tools can be attached to the business end; it is immensely powerful and unbelievably manoeuvrable. It can virtually pirouette on the spot.

When it first appeared, it was usually hired for short periods but it is becoming increasingly a necessary part of standard equipment on the modern mechanical farm.

There are some places where even a skid-steer isn't much good. Where the old byres are still in use, a gripe and a wheelbarrow and a pair of strong arms are necessary. The manure is being taken to a walled midden. From there, modern technology takes over.

Foddering sheep

Autumn, winter and spring are cold up here, and usually windy. That's par for the course. The farmer can usually handle a few days of snow and take it in his stride. He's used to that. Sharp frosts are wonderful because that goes with dry weather and the stock take no harm in such conditions. There might even be the opportunity to get ahead in the muck-spreading schedule. It's long wet spells that make the work really miserable.

Between December and April the hill farmer cannot avoid being out in the elements as a large part of each day is taken up carrying winter fodder to his stock. After weeks of wet weather the ground is waterlogged. Walk over the land and water oozes up to the ankles of your boots. Further rain can't soak into the ground; it just runs off in sheets. The stock is wet. Even the air is thick with water vapour.

Weather like this is a challenge for any protective clothing. The hill farmer just knows that water is going to get in somewhere, and soon after going out he knows he'll be soaked to the skin. He can't get any wetter, so he gets on with the job.

If all the hay were dumped in one heap this operation would turn into a big woolly rugby scrum. Some sheep would get more than their fair share and others would get none. A pitchfork is handy to break up the bales and spread the hay over a wide area. On a windy fellside it may be necessary to use hayracks, but these bring their own problems. An adequate number would be needed to allow enough room for all to feed, and the racks would need to be moved at regular intervals as the ground around them would become broken, muddy and soiled.

"Sheep hay" needs to be special. It must be well made, nutritious and palatable. Cattle in their winter quarters will eat virtually anything put before them and relish it. Sheep, on the other hand, have an option. If they don't like the hay they will ignore it and carry on grazing the sparse, poor quality winter herbage.

This hay seems to be getting the "thumbs up".

Nature conservancy

Although often tragically denied much of a formal education, and sentenced by fate to spend most of their lives underground in damp, unhealthy conditions, there were leadminers who had amazing intellectual ability. In their limited spare time they became amateur artists, poets, craftsmen and scientists. One such character was John Binks, who in about 1750 realised that there was something special in the botany of upper Teesdale. He passed on some of his knowledge and specimens to the local doctor and vicar, who realised the importance of his work and forwarded them to Kew, where they caused much excitement.

A quirk of geology, climate and traditional hill farming practices has preserved the ecology. For 22 years, Ian Findlay was the officer of the Nature Conservancy in Teesdale, monitoring and caring for this very special part of our heritage.

It was the intrusion of a huge band of igneous rock (the "Great Whin Sill") into the limestone of the Pennines two hundred and fifty million years ago, and subsequent development of the surrounding hills, which created these truly unique conditions. But it was the sound sustainable management by the hill farmer that allowed them to endure. There was mixed grazing by cattle and sheep, and no overgrazing. The hay season was late, allowing the flora to seed and flourish before it was cut.

It was a major part of Ian's brief to liaise with the hill farmers, balancing farm economics and practices with the need to protect this great asset. His wisdom and knowledge were well suited to the job, but his enthusiasm was a bonus. He once counted 156 different botanical species in a single hay meadow, and even now, several years after his retirement, he records daily the intimate details of the weather.

Summer

The Pennines are an awesome sight at any time of the day or year, but there are evenings in the summer that are very special. Towards the end of a warm, still, summer's day the hills can assume a unique beauty.

My wife, Chris, and I have made something of a study of the phenomenon. When the evening sun is still fiercely bright in a clear sky and the heat of the day throws up an ethereal haze on the western horizon, we head for the hills and spend a couple of hours soaking up the tranquillity and splendour of the landscape. We sit and watch. Perhaps we see a short-eared owl quartering his beat, or a curlew paragliding across the sky. We once watched a stoat carefully rolling a pheasant's egg across the road in front of us. He flicked it up into the tussocks on the verge and disappeared into the undergrowth to find a secluded spot where he could tuck into his plunder.

But the last half-hour before sunset is magic. Gradually the setting sun dips into the haze. Its brightness fades and it slowly transforms into a golden orb, scattering diminishing light across the serried ranks of Pennine hills.

The spring rush is over. Calving, lambing, muck-spreading, harrowing and winter feeding are behind him. The hill farmer can relax – a little – and enjoy the dale at its mellow best. The fields turn gold with buttercups and marsh marigolds. Lambs are growing rapidly. Swallows scythe through the sky, while meadow pipits hop to and fro along the tops of the drystone walls.

However, the sheep are to be gathered and sheared, after which it's time to think about next winter's rations. Grass growth is slow to start and there's seldom enough to cut until mid-July. This fact accounts for the botanical richness of the upland meadows for it gives the plants time to mature and seed. Haymaking used to be a frantic, labour intensive affair with a wet July and August spelling disaster. Mechanisation, big bales and silage production have taken much of the uncertainty out of it.

By mid-September the summer is over. In some years it feels as though spring, summer and autumn have been squeezed into four or five months.

The summer landscape

More than forty years on I still recall with ease geography lessons at school, where we were required to recite the names of the rivers flowing into the Yorkshire Ouse: Swale, Wharfe, Ure, Aire, Nidd, Calder, Don. Add to the list Tees, Wear, and Tyne that find their own way to the sea, and you have a complete list of the major rivers which flow eastwards from the northern Pennines. The latter three arise within a few miles of each other near Alston, reputedly the highest market town in the country.

All of these rivers have their beginnings as trickles from the big mossy sponge which caps the high hills and carve their way through rocky passages and cataracts in the upper dales. As they hit the foothills of their parent range their course suddenly becomes more leisurely, and bends in grand bows through grassy pastures.

Their east to west carving leaves high east to west ridges, which, before the days of motorised transport, formed a natural geographical barrier between the parallel dales. A visit to north or south would necessitate a steep ascent, a precipitous descent, a journey of fifteen or twenty miles, and serious wear on horseshoes or footwear. It was so much easier to stay within the confines of one's native patch. Each valley, thus formed, became a cradle of its own culture, a crucible containing a dialect, folklore, architecture and industries, with subtle differences from neighbours to north and south. The geology of each dale and the building skills of the inhabitants gave rise to fieldhouses and drystone walls of disparate character. There are subtle differences in the flavour of the fare on offer. In Hawes you can buy a unique cheese, and slabs of bacon with hardly a hint of lean meat in them – staple fare a century ago, and still available.

Market towns such as Hawes, Leyburn, Barnard Castle, Skipton and Reeth are little gems. They retain to this day the magic of a bygone era when everyone knew their neighbour – and was probably related to them!

Rocky outcrops on the high hills, wooded valleys, drystone walls and Swaledale sheep: a picture that attracts visitors in their thousands to the upper dales in summer. Tranquil places such as Hawes, Reeth and Kettlewell burst at the seams with stout-booted disciples of Wainwright who have come to enjoy and be invigorated by the clear air and the breathtaking scenery.

The visitor is welcomed to the dales, and much has been done to make his visit a pleasant one. Footpaths are clearly marked, old railway lines have been adapted to become walkways and cycleways, information boards tell of the topography and natural history. Most towns and some of the villages have attractive tourist information centres.

The Pennine Way has created an opportunity for the more energetic to become better acquainted with the high fells. Brightly coloured anoraks in Indian file punctuate the greys and browns of the landscape the whole year round.

There are minor inconveniences to the hill farmer. The narrow country roads were not intended for heavy traffic, and occasionally a well-trodden footpath passes right through the middle of a farmyard. However, the advantages of a healthy tourist industry far outweigh the disadvantages. In these days of modest financial returns from agriculture, the hill farmer is well placed to provide services and hospitality for the tourist, and in so doing generate a second source of income.

Farmhouse bed and breakfast has always been popular and in recent years roadside signs advertising the facility have proliferated. Redundant farm buildings have been tastefully converted to attractive holiday cottages, an operation encouraged by the English Tourist Board and other similar bodies. Taken a step further, leisure facilities can be developed too. Riding and pony trekking centres are the most obvious, but one enterprising farmer has recently set up an "off-road" driving school which looks like being a great success.

The hill farmer has always been adaptable and it could be that investing some of his time and energy in visitors could be, at least, a part of his strategy for survival through difficult times.

As summer progresses the dales landscape is ever changing.

Haymaking, crucial for the winter welfare of the stock, is in full swing. There are the green fields that have not yet been cut, and the slightly paler green of freshly mown meadows. The green is slowly turning to yellow where the hay is being made, and the parched pale browns mark the cleared fields. The whole vista resembles a patchwork quilt. The squares are neatly divided by the stitchwork of the drystone walls. The hand of man is once more dipping into its palette and adding its brush strokes to the vast canvas of the dales.

Kirk Carrion, Lunedale. The steep dales pastures are clad in their summer green, and at the summit are crowned by a striking clump of trees, serving as a reminder of the hill farmers of long ago. The trees replaced a tumulus – a huge cairn of large loose stones. When the cairn was removed in 1804, it revealed a funeral urn containing human bone fragments, probably those of a Bronze Age chieftain.

It is thought that man had come to these hills in the Mesolithic period as a Stone Age hunter-gatherer. By burning he created clearings in the dense woodland, and deforestation would continue until, by the end of the Bronze Age, the high fells were largely devoid of trees. Studies of pollen preserved in peat point to a gradual disappearance of oak and alder, and its replacement by grass and heather during the last 2000 years BC. Our chieftain probably lived about 1500BC, and it is from this period that we see the first hill farmers in the upper dales. The settlements were sparsely scattered and seem to have each consisted of a single large "round-house" surrounded by a series of irregular enclosures. This would suggest that our early hill farmer kept stock or grew crops and probably did both.

At the time of the Roman invasion of AD43, nothing much had changed. There were still no villages, and the farms were still isolated units. There were, however, more of them, and the farmers were growing oats and some types of wheat. They could also smelt and work iron. Almost all of the large forests had gone.

Thus began the long tradition of hill farming in the Pennines.

Summer visitors

In the winter the uplands can be the bleakest of places with very few signs of life. There are the sheep, of course, and the red grouse which are welded to the heather moors for twelve months of the year. The farmer pays a brief visit to fodder the sheep, and there's the occasional scavenging carrion crow. Apart from that, there's nothing.

And then, in the course of a few weeks in the spring, the place is transformed.

Pipits and wheatears hop along the tops of the drystone walls. The skylark's bubbling music ascends skywards. The air is filled with the calls of the returning waders. There's the hysterical song-flight of the peewit, the plaintive whistle of the golden plover, the shrill notes of the oystercatcher, and even the drumming wing-beats of the displaying snipe. But there's nothing to match the call of the curlew, so characteristic of the dales.

The curlews arrive in early March, two or three weeks after the peewits. They travel in small groups, calling to each other as though keeping in contact. Such is the urgency of their instinct to return to the breeding grounds that many travel through the night, and can be heard calling as they pass overhead.

Having arrived, they set up their territories. Their displays are a joy to behold. They make fast, sweeping passes almost at ground level, then mount high in the air as though climbing an invisible ladder. At the apex of the climb they spread their wings like a hang-glider and float gracefully halfway back to the ground before once again beginning their ascent.

This is a redshank, another of the long-billed, long-legged summer visitors to the hill farm's upland pastures. These birds are all very wary by nature, and for eleven months of the year are exceedingly difficult to approach. But they are also extremely diligent parents. Since the young, from day one, can move about freely and find their own food, the main role of the parents is that of sentinel. At the approach of danger, the parents' warning calls will freeze the well-camouflaged chicks into immobility.

It is at this stage when they will use the top of a drystone wall as a watchtower. Their innate shyness gives way to parental instincts. They will hold their ground, using their elevated position to keep an eye on their precious young, and to assess the danger from the intruder with the telephoto lens pointing out of the car window.

The well thumbed, constant companion of my boyhood, *The Observer's Book of British Birds*, makes interesting reading almost fifty years on. It tells us that the oystercatcher is a handsome bird, typical of the rocky and sandy shore. It tells us that its nest is a few bits of broken shells in shingle or rocks, and very rarely in grass near the coast. Its food is described as sandworms, shellfish, crustaceans, tiny fish, and shrimps. At the time it was totally accurate, but in the last two or three decades, the oystercatcher has joined its wader colleagues in the mass exodus of shore birds that come to visit the hill farmer each spring.

When I first heard the distinctive, loud, high-pitched call in the skies of the dales, I could hardly believe my ears. A sighting confirmed its identity. Since then it has come in increasing numbers.

In 1974, three pairs nested in the locality. Today there must be over a hundred.

"What's up when it's down and down when it's up" goes the old country conundrum.

And the answer, of course, is the crest on a peewit's head, which lies flat when the bird is in flight but stands erect when the bird alights.

The peewit is among the first of the waders to return to its breeding grounds in the hills. Even in wintry mid-February the peewit flocks with their plodding wing-beats are a welcome sight, for it does mean that spring is on its way. Soon afterwards the males will set up their territories, and in the process treat us all to an exciting aerobatic display. Crazily zigzagging, they hurtle noisily through the sky, rolling, diving and plunging.

Both male and female are excellent parents, shepherding and guarding their three or four precocious chicks. In spite of this, predation by gulls, crows and stoats causes devastating losses.

When I was a small boy I kept a "nature notebook" and in it I recorded my first sightings of all the summer visitors. The swallows always arrived on 25th of April, but they have made their appearance a little earlier each year since then. I love to hear the busy twittering on returning from their fix of winter sun in North Africa. The farmer has a soft spot for them too as the same birds return to the same nesting spot each year.

In one byre in the practice there is a little wicker basket nailed to a roof beam. The farmer found a dislodged nest containing four young on the byre floor, improvised the new support, and replaced the nest. The family was raised successfully and the basket has been used every year since then.

The picture shows an unusually large brood of seven.

Shorthorns

For centuries the Teeswater or "Durham Breed" had dominated the Pennine landscape until, in the early 1800s, the Colling family refined the breed to what we now recognise as the Shorthorn. Towards the end of that century further refinements resulted in divergence of the breed into a meat producing strain (Beef Shorthorn) and a milk producing strain (Northern Dairy Shorthorn).

For decades the Northern Dairy Shorthorn was to reign supreme. The breed was ideally suited to flourish on the upland pastures, and survives in isolated pockets to this day. An elegant pair of horns was a much-prized feature.

The Northern Dairy Shorthorn bull.
It has always been a great puzzle to me
that bulls of the dairy breeds have fiery
temperaments yet produce daughters
with a placid disposition. The converse
is also true. Bulls of the beef breeds are
relatively easy to handle but can sire
daughters with a serious attitude
problem.

This fellow was not to be trusted but
fortunately was accommodated in a
purpose built (and very safe) bull pen.
Nevertheless, taking a blood sample
from him for brucellosis testing every
two years was quite exciting!

A mere fifty years ago this would have
been a typical dales landscape, except
that the cows would each have had a pair
of spectacular horns. Some breeders
even used metal clamps to train, gently,
the horns of young heifers to grow in the
right direction.

Bull hire

When Alan Scott was a boy on his father's farm, there were always two bulls. Neighbouring farmers were aware of this spare capacity and knew that they were welcome to take advantage of it. Thus it was a common occurrence for a neighbour to turn up at the Scotts' farm with a cow on a halter, having walked perhaps two or three miles to procure the services of the spare bull. It often fell to Alan to oversee the alliance and he recalls long periods "hanging about in a windy farmyard" waiting for the bull to do what bulls do.

Years later, in a flash of entrepreneurial inspiration, he realised that there was a business opportunity here. It would make good sense to acquire a few good quality bulls and make them available for hire. In the hill farmer's beef suckler herd, most cows calve in the spring so a bull is needed only for a few weeks in the summer months. By hiring, the farmer could procure the services of a quality bull which he would normally not be able to afford. He would also avoid the necessary maintenance and welfare of the animal during the eight or nine months when it was not being used.

There would be advantages for Alan too. The bulls could be used all the year round – in the autumn on dairy heifers which produce August calves, and in the winter on suckler herds which have an autumn calving pattern.

Alan's business has gone from strength to strength and he now has about eighty bulls for hire. They are housed in a large building with sturdy bull pens and safe, purpose-designed handling facilities.

The setting up of a bull-hire business was a brilliant and successful idea, advantageous to all concerned.

However it was not a new one.

Two hundred years ago, the famous Robert Bakewell hit on the notion. Bakewell's influence on agriculture was revolutionary, for he devoted his working life to improving scientifically the quality of agricultural livestock by breeding towards desirable genetic traits. He and his colleagues pioneered the "letting-out" of sires. They set up annual exhibitions of bulls, rams and stallions which could be purchased outright or hired for a year. The practice of hiring was beneficial because the genetic material of a good quality sire would be available in different places each year and could improve the quality of stock over a wide area during its lifetime.

The variety of Alan's stock is dictated by demand and the demand is for the large, rapidly growing bulls of the continental breeds. Charolais (seen here), Limousin, Blonde d'Aquitaine, Belgian Blue and Simmental are the popular breeds. However, it is encouraging to note that the traditional British breeds are making something of a comeback and now account for a quarter of Alan's stock.

The bulls are hired out for varying periods but most will be away for seven to ten weeks.

Dairying

There used to be a milk stand like this at the roadside by almost every dales farm. Dairy herds with cow numbers in single figures were commonplace. The daily yield would be carefully filtered, cooled, and run into these ten-gallon containers which were placed on the milk stand each morning. The milk lorry with its dozens of rattling cans was a familiar sight on the dales roads.

A monthly "milk cheque" was a welcome aid to cash flow since income from beef and sheep enterprises arrived only a few times each year.

The milk lorry with its rattling cans is a distant memory. Filters, coolers and cans have disappeared from the farm dairy to be replaced by large refrigerated stainless steel tanks.

Today huge tankers with computerised pumps collect the yield of the dairy industry, but such vehicles are rarely seen in most parts of the high Pennines. Small-scale dairying on marginal land is an increasingly difficult way to make a living. The upland dairy unit has not, however, disappeared altogether and the milk tanker's journey still takes it across the heather moors.

More years ago than I care to remember there were long summer holidays from school and college. Each year I usually managed to spend a month or so "working for my keep" on a small farm in the Eden valley. It was a wonderful break from the academic life. At five o'clock I'd cycle down the lane to bring in the cows for milking. Most of them knew what time it was and would be waiting at the field gate for me. They also knew the way home. My only useful function was to open the gate.

In the reign of the Shorthorn this would have been quite a different picture. The cattle would have been red, white or various in-between shades of roan. A resident of neighbouring Lunedale told me, "We didn't see a black and white cow here till 1955."

To be in dairying you have to like cows. If you didn't it would be an awful chore milking them twice a day, seven days a week and fifty two weeks a year. Some of the older generation were proud of the fact that they'd not missed a milking for decades.

Farmwatch

About ten years ago the dales were suffering visits of epidemic proportions from criminals. Trailers, quad bikes, power tools, Land Rovers and even livestock were disappearing overnight. The police were doing their best but in the rural environment with hundreds of square miles to patrol they couldn't be everywhere.

Peter Stubbs and his wife Gladys decided to start a "Farmwatch" scheme. Cynics labelled it as a short-lived gimmick. Five years later, and after remarkable success, formal co-ordination with the county constabulary brought even more amazing results. Peter regularly raises forty members who keep all-night vigils to monitor the movements of suspicious vehicles.

Full and formal co-operation with the police has been a key factor in the ongoing success of the project. The success is such that the local scheme has formed a role model for similar organisations all over the UK. The most recent development is that a mobile police station has been made available on "operations" nights. Radio communications between members within the dale are good but until now would not extend to neighbouring dales. The mobile office parked up on high ground will relay radio messages and information over a much wider area.

Success breeds success. From the early days of the project when a few members would spend the night parked up in gateways and make a call on a mobile phone if they saw anything suspicious, the operations have become much more sophisticated. NFU Mutual donated £10,000 to provide radio telephones so that there is instant communication between all vehicles keeping vigil. Night vision equipment has been made available, and there is access to a "Crime Ring" computer to disseminate information.

Peter's philosophy when he set up the group is well worth a quote – "If you're not seen to be helping yourselves you're not going to get help from anyone else".

Diversification

The hill farmer is renowned for his hard work and resilience but the latter quality has been sorely tested in recent years by events far beyond his control and far from the northern hills.

Who would have thought that the fall of the Berlin Wall would have sent out ripples across the North Sea, which made waves in the high Pennines years later? But it did. The events in Berlin heralded the disintegration of the USSR and the collapse of the Russian economy. Overnight a market for thousands of sheepskins disappeared. The strength of sterling, directives from Brussels, bureaucracy from Westminster, and BSE all had negative effects on farmers' morale and bank balances.

Whilst some of the older generation have pulled forward their retirement dates and sold up, those remaining have shown great character and adaptability.

Trevor, like many hill farmers, has spent a lot of time building and repairing drystone walls. Some years ago he thought it would be fun to adapt his traditional skills to produce miniature representations.

At first the enterprise was little more than a hobby but a friend who owned a local hotel persuaded him to display some of his pieces. They proved so popular that Trevor stepped up his output and "Dalestone Crafts" was born. His hobby had become a thriving cottage industry. His wares are now sold at craft fairs and agricultural shows throughout the north of England.

As "Dalestone Crafts" developed Trevor incorporated scale model sheep, lambs and collies into his creations, making his tableaux even more attractive and authentic. Each piece is unique, handmade by Trevor, and captures cleverly the flavour of the dales landscape. As his raw material he uses sandstone cut from local quarries. Visitors from as far afield as the USA, Canada, Australia and New Zealand have bought examples of his work.

For decades the hill farmer has been pressured into "running faster to stand still". He has been advised to opt for bigger, faster-maturing cattle and sheep. These in turn are more expensive to cater for.

Recently there has been a movement towards more organic sustainable farming using hardy traditional breeds to produce a low cost, high quality product. Already there are those who have chosen this option and have proved that it can be a great success.

Brian Scott has gone for diversification in a big way.

Brian is a trained butcher and has opened a butcher's shop on his farm in a remote corner of the dale. Much of his produce is home reared. However, Brian's entrepreneurial expertise extends to far more than the butcher's shop. Many years ago he converted a disused barn into a "bunkhouse". Hikers travelling the Pennine Way can make an overnight stop there. The facilities are ideal for the backpacker needing only somewhere to cook, shower and lay out a sleeping bag.

His latest enterprise is a restaurant in a converted building on the farmstead.

Shearing

Clipping days used to be great social occasions. Dozens of neighbours and their families would congregate at the farm where the shearing was to take place. Twenty to thirty men might be wielding the shears. Others would be penning the sheep, catching them to present to the shearers, or wrapping fleeces. Special food and drink were provided in abundance and in the evening there would be music and dancing.

Nowadays at the top of the dale the clipping is more of a family affair, with all hands on deck and a few neighbours along to help. Electric shears have made the job much quicker and easier but the art of using the old hand shears is still alive and well.

Hand shears such as those we see here have been used since Roman times. The operator begins in the standing position and holds the sheep in a sitting position while he clips the belly, neck and forequarters. He then generally goes down on one knee to clip down the back, over the hindquarters and finishes with the tail.

Whilst hand shears are useful for the odd sheep that has missed the clipping, virtually all sheep are shorn with electric shears now. Gone are the days of the big social occasions, and in many cases the work is contracted out to teams of sheepshearers. Teams of two or three are the norm on the average hill farm. The professionals work very quickly and it's hot, backache-inducing labour.

Although the farmer is not actually doing the shearing, he and his family are kept busy penning, catching and presenting the sheep to the operators. Someone is also required to wrap each fleece.

As soon as the shearing is completed a paint mark is applied. When the sheep are returned to the fell they tend to stay on their own "heaf" but some do stray. Wanderers can be inadvertently gathered with someone else's flock so that unique identification for each farm is important.

All sheep in this flock have a "T" burned into the left horn, an "A" burned into the right horn, a green ear tag in the left ear, a red rud mark on the left buttock, and an "X", as you can see, on the right buttock.

Sheep dipping

The sheep's thick fleece would seem an ideal environment for a range of parasites, so it's little wonder that a variety of little creatures have evolved to live happily there. Mites, lice and keds have caused problems for centuries, and the shepherd has waged a constant battle against them. Until relatively recent times the only measures available for their control was the laborious application of a salve of oil and tar. A gallon of tar and seventeen pounds of butter would be sufficient for about twenty five sheep. It was only in the middle of the 19th century that the practice of dipping was adopted.

Parasitic diseases had such a serious effect on the welfare of the sheep and the economics of the farmer that a compulsory dipping order was introduced in 1905. The main offender was, and is, a tiny skin-dwelling mite which causes "sheep scab". The mite could lie dormant during the summer months, but in colder weather it would become active and cause intense irritation. Badly infected sheep would rub and scratch dementedly till the fleece was in tatters and the skin covered in abrasions. The sheep would become emaciated, and in extreme circumstances, die.

The statutory dipping order succeeded in controlling the disease and the UK was declared free from sheep scab in 1952. However, it reappeared in 1973, apparently via some imported sheep, and has been with us since then.

Dipping came frustratingly close to achieving total eradication of sheep scab. In theory it should have, for by law every sheep in the country had to be dipped and the rules were stringently policed. The village constable would be present at the dipping to ensure that the procedure was carried out to the letter of the law. Later, the local authority took over the policing role.

Statutory controls were removed in 1991 and, after 86 years of diligent counter measures, sheep scab spread alarmingly. Fortunately there are now injectable preparations which can treat affected sheep.

Haymaking

William Fothergill, in the *General View of Agriculture of the North Riding*, wrote of dales farming in 1794:

"Hay is the grand object of the farmer and he bestows upon it his most sedulous attention and has many difficulties to combat. The season commences late, the surrounding hills occasion frequent showers, and the meadows, which are all natural, abound with herbs which, being more succulent than the grasses, are more difficult to harvest."

Haymaking before mechanisation (a mere 60 or 70 years ago) was a laborious business and could take up all of the summer months. The cutting was done with scythes, often wielded by itinerant hired labourers. Strewing, turning and gathering into pikes were all subsequently accomplished by hours of painstaking toil with hands, rakes and forks. A spell of rain at the wrong moment would mean that the whole process would have to be repeated.

Mowing a steep-sided dales hay meadow. The mower has produced a bizarre pattern on the hillside as he avoided the "sykes" or deep gullies where a spring emerges from the hillside and makes its way to the beck below.

Most of the upper dales hay meadows have been designated as "Environmentally Sensitive Areas" and the Ministry of Agriculture operates a scheme which reconciles modern farming practices with the need to protect the flora and the ground-nesting birds. The scheme is quite complex but its main points are concerned with limiting application of artificial fertilisers and postponement of grass cutting until mid-July. By then the upland flora will have matured and seeded. Ground-nesting birds will also have completed their breeding cycle.

This looks like haymaking weather. The grass has been cut and allowed to wilt in the heat of the sun before being evenly scattered or "strewn" over the field to complete the drying process. It is at this stage that the hay is at its most vulnerable to a soaking. Rain on the thick freshly cut swaths is not a disaster but bad weather at this stage can have a devastating effect on the quality of the stock's winter sustenance. If the weather holds fair for a day or two longer, this hay crop will be perfect.

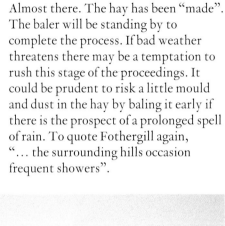

Almost there. The hay has been "made". The baler will be standing by to complete the process. If bad weather threatens there may be a temptation to rush this stage of the proceedings. It could be prudent to risk a little mould and dust in the hay by baling it early if there is the prospect of a prolonged spell of rain. To quote Fothergill again, "… the surrounding hills occasion frequent showers".

Rowing up is completed and the bales are being churned out. It's hard to imagine that little more than fifty years ago the baler was a new and revolutionary tool in agriculture. The very first models were static. They were drawn into the hayfield and the hay was brought to the baler with sweeps to be fed into the jaws of the machine.

A tractor roars along rowing up with a baler in hot pursuit. The advent of the mobile baler using the tractor as its power source must have seemed like a miracle. Whilst the old balers had used wire to bind the hay, the new ones used sisal string. And what would our eponymous hero have done without sisal string? I'm sure that an academic could do his PhD on the subject.

Right. What a poignant picture. It tells us of progress. The familiar square bale which brought a revolutionary change to the life of the hill farmer a few decades ago is already becoming obsolete.

The elevator lies rusting where it last saw action. The barn is no longer the store for the precious winter rations. High technology silage making and big round bales are becoming the order of the day. It's a poignant picture, yes. But it's not a sad picture. The hill farmer may value tradition, but he's also swift to embrace innovation and benefit from the advantages. As a Luddite he would not have survived. His modern mechanical farm needs to be efficient. The old square bales were moved by hand four or five times between field and manger. A big bale impaled on a foreloader makes much more sense.

The hay crop has been successfully baled. Good quality winter fodder has been secured. All that remains to be done is to "lead" it to the barn. It's quite often an evening job when family and friends are available to lend a hand. And speaking of hands, that sisal string is cruel to them!

This is a relatively new sight in the dales landscape. It reflects other changes too. Even the most casual observer on journeys in the countryside must have noticed the large cattle sheds that have sprung up like mushrooms on every farmstead in recent years. These buildings allow the cattle to move about, to exercise and socialise – yes, cattle *do* socialise. But the big sheds are also ideal for efficient mechanised feeding and bedding systems and it is here that big bale and big building go hand in hand.

Sadly this has accounted for the demise of the traditional cowshed or byre. Even in the bleakest winter the byre was a warm and cosy place with memories of summer evoked by scents wafting from the hayloft.

The big hay bale can be impaled on a spike on the foreloader of a tractor and carried anywhere. One man in a very short time can move large quantities of fodder in one simple operation.

There were some desperately bad haymaking seasons in the early 70s. Hay lay in the fields for weeks, some with fresh grass growing through the swaths. I remember seeing one hill farmer trying to salvage his crop in October. The hay was a blackish brown colour and as he rowed it up to prepare it for baling clouds of white fungal spores flew into the air. It was a bad winter for the stock that year. The nutritive value of the hay was minimal and there were some very poor cattle turned out the following spring. The dust and fungal spores were a health hazard to the farmer too.

Such a scenario will never be repeated, thanks to modern technology and the big bale. The hill farmer now has a second option, a safety net.

In a good summer with favourable weather, haymaking can proceed as normal. However, he can now cut his haycrop when the grass is at its best. If the weather doesn't favour the production of hay he can make half dried grass into big bales and wrap them in plastic. In that state the fodder will retain its nutritive value. Good quality winter rations are assured.

Autumn

The classic landscape photographer is an artist. His eye for composition is inspired. He knows what the scene will look like on his "canvas". He will set up his tripod at just the right spot. And he will wait. He will wait until the sunlight and the clouds conspire to mix the right colours for his palette. Then, and only then, will he press the shutter. He has created his masterpiece.

My landscape photography bears no resemblance to the products of such sophisticated technique. But I do have one distinct advantage. The life of a country vet has taken me out on the road at all hours of the day and night. Travelling up to thirty thousand miles each year in the dales with a camera on the passenger seat of the car presents some wonderful opportunities to capture a moment of beauty in the Pennines. I've taken many of my most pleasing pictures at six o'clock on a morning, on the way home for breakfast after dealing with an emergency case.

If I were a hill farmer, I would find autumn the most agreeable of seasons. The heather moors are still purple, the rowan trees splash the gills with vivid colour, the hay is safely stowed in the barn and the winter chores are weeks away. It is also the most convivial of seasons. The young folk take days off to earn some pocket money beating for the grouse-shooting parties, there are family outings to the agricultural shows, and there are the Swaledale tup sales.

The tup sales at Hawes, Kirkby Stephen, Middleton and St John's Chapel are important dates in the hill farmer's calendar. They are huge gatherings of knowledgeable stockmen whose expertise has elevated the Swaledale, in just a few decades, from humble mountain sheep to foundation stock on which much of the British sheep industry is based. The hill farmer is immensely proud of the breed. He knows the family trees of most of the hundreds of sheep presented for sale, and will make measured decisions on which tup will be purchased to turn out with his ewes in November.

Autumn gales will soon strip the trees; the stock will exhaust the late flush of grass and the hill farmer will steel himself to the task of husbanding his animals through winter.

The autumn landscape

Season of mists and mellow fruitfulness,
Close bosom-friend of the maturing sun.

The words of John Keats in his ode *To Autumn* are familiar to us all. However, I don't think Keats was thinking of the high Pennines when he wrote those lines. The hill farmer would be quick to point out to him that we've plenty of mists, but are a little short in the "mellow fruitfulness" stakes. Rose-hips and blackberries do put on a show in the hedgerows. Bilberries can be plentiful on the moor, although if you want to make a pie you need to be pretty quick to beat the flocks of wood pigeons which come to feast on them.

Autumn can be the briefest of seasons in these parts. By the time the last of the season's agricultural shows has finished in mid-September, you realise that the swallows have gone and the flocks of fieldfares have arrived from Scandinavia. The wading birds, pipits, and merlin have vacated the moors, leaving the sole rights to the red grouse.

It's not unknown for the first snows to come in October.

The light in the Pennines can play some bizarre tricks. Here a mist is rolling down the valley. Combined with a setting sun, it throws into stark silhouette a typical dales farmstead.

Trees are not a major feature of the Pennine landscape, but pictures like this portray how clusters of huge mature sycamores and ashes seem to occur in farm garths. Elsewhere they are thinly distributed or even absent. For a while this phenomenon puzzled me but I think the answer is fairly obvious. The fields around the farmstead are seldom without cattle or sheep in them, and any little sapling would be snipped off by the teeth of a grazing animal.

However, I think the hill farmer likes his sycamores and is happy to see them growing in the farmyard. Apart from their beauty, they provide shade in the summer and shelter from winter's winds. Many farmers used to be keen bee-keepers, and some still are. In May the tree's flowers provide a rich source of nectar. And when, at last, the old tree is past its best and the trunk begins to rot, it can be felled to provide several tons of firewood.

Grouse shooting

The heather moors of Scotland and the Northern Pennines have a majestic beauty. It is hard to imagine that the hand of Man has worked this beauty and is responsible for creating this awesome landscape.

Virtually all of these hills were originally covered by forest. Over the centuries these forests were cleared and sheep then grazed the land. The shepherds found that by burning off the old heather, young highly nutritious shoots would be encouraged to grow. Thus burning and grazing prevented the landscape reverting to its natural state and the unique ecosystem that we see today was created. Today the moors are managed for the benefit of both sheep and grouse.

Since the advent of the railways (providing easy access to the north) grouse shooting has enjoyed a strong following and has contributed to the economy of the dales. Members of farming families often gain full time employment as keepers or estate workers, while during the "season" there is part time work as domestic staff, beaters, flankers and loaders.

The moor sustains an incredibly diverse flora and fauna, but the dominant plant by far is the common heather (*Calluna vulgaris*). Vast carpets of the plant stretch from horizon to horizon. The winter landscape is stark and inhospitable, but in the spring myriad songbirds and waders will flock to these hills to breed. However, the summer is short. In early August, after four months of frantic activity, the immigrants leave. As if in celebration, and with a huge sigh of relief, the moor erupts into a blaze of purple. The heady scent of nectar and pollen is everywhere.

From April through to August, the cock red grouse keeps a low profile. During those months his plumage is dull and he, along with his mate, concentrates his energies on diligent parental duties. Then suddenly, and in synchrony with his heather moor, he sheds his drab mantle to moult from camouflage order into full dress uniform. Family responsibilities are put aside. His proclivity for territorial existence comes to the fore. For the next eight months, he will ensure that the whole world is aware of his presence.

The late summer air resounds to the call "Go back, go back, go back". Like Jekyll and Hyde, the quiet family man has turned into fierce aggressor. He lays claim to exclusive rights on a five acre patch of this vast landscape. He will defend it with tireless energy, attract a mate, and raise his family there.

Territorial behaviour. From an elevated vantage point in the centre of his territory, the cock grouse will noisily announce his claim and keep a diligent watch. At the approach of an intruder the crimson combs dilate, the body is raised to its full height, and a deep throaty almost human grumble warns of the incumbent's displeasure. Should the intrusion persist, the angered cock bird takes to the wing. The flight is fast, low and direct. At the last moment, as he approaches the point of threat, the low flight path changes to a vertical soar. At the top of the soar the tail is widely fanned and the wings held akimbo.

The chest is puffed out and the head held high. The notes of displeasure are reiterated with the volume turned up to maximum. The body language and noisy protestations make it formidably clear that visitors are not welcome.

Should the interloper be a neighbouring male with aspirations to extending his adjacent territory there follows the most animated and often humorous confrontation. Both birds bob and strut along an invisible dividing line between the territories. They gobble and hiss like disgruntled farmyard turkeys. It is obvious that they are hurling abuse at each other.

August is the month which everyone associates with the grouse. Even those who have never seen a grouse moor cannot escape the ballyhoo and high profile media coverage of the "Glorious Twelfth".

The shooting in the early season is of the highest quality. The sportsman in his butt will be presented with small packs, perhaps family groups of five to twelve individuals. These driven birds fly low, hugging the contours of the landscape at speeds sometimes exceeding sixty miles an hour.

Shooting in September takes on a rather changed character from that of the opening month. The small groups tend to gather into larger packs. At the same time the older cock birds' family instincts are on the wane. Their proclivity for territorial existence results in their leaving these large groups.

Thus in September the guns are presented with a mixture of packs and singletons. Since a singleton is more likely to be shot than a bird in a large group, a higher proportion of old cock birds tend to appear in the bag.

In a year when grouse are abundant it is important to keep up the shooting pressure to reduce stocks to a level which can be sustained by the moor over winter. Conversely when stocks are low, shooting must be curtailed long before the tenth of December, the official end of the season.

The "gun" and his loader in a butt. It is standard practice for the grouse shooter to use a matched pair of 12-bore double-barrelled shotguns. Towards the end of a drive there can be intense activity and the loader will have a well-rehearsed routine for quickly exchanging a loaded gun for an empty one.

Butts come in varying shapes, sizes and design depending on where they are sited. This one is in an exposed spot on a hillside and has been sunk and turfed to render it less obvious.

A classic view down the line of the butts. Lines of about ten are sited at several points on the grouse moor. The terrain, the season, and the prevailing weather conditions will dictate which lines will be used on the shooting day.

The beaters will be positioned by the head keeper in a large semicircle of perhaps more than a mile in radius. At a given signal all move towards the guns. Communication and co-ordination of the beaters is quite a complicated process but in recent years mobile radios have become widely used.

The butts are generally placed about fifty yards apart and it can be seen that a strict code of conduct must be in place to ensure the safety of everyone on the moor. The guns may take birds in front and behind the line of butts but must raise the gun in between so that at no time does the gun point down the line. "Swinging through" is a serious misdemeanour.

As the beaters approach the butts, the head keeper will signal no more forward shooting by giving a loud blast on a horn or whistle.

Rough shooting

Frank's annual shoot is something of a special occasion. It's a farmers' shoot. A dozen guns are invited to walk about three hundred acres of his rugged but breathtakingly beautiful marginal land. Alder-filled and rock-strewn gills carve their way through rushy pastures. Blackthorn thickets and birch copses punctuate the landscape; and dividing the pastures are the hawthorn hedges, many of them trained to a forty five degree angle by the Pennine winds.

The sport is totally different to the formal driven shoot where large numbers of artificially-reared birds are accounted for. The game is wild and wary up here. A pheasant might break cover from a wooded gill flying high and fast. A rabbit might bolt from any of the tussocks in a reed-strewn meadow. Woodcock, duck, snipe or partridge may give a brief opportunity for a shot.

With hedges and huge patches of rushes to hunt through, and game to retrieve from difficult terrain, I'd often leave my gun at home and enjoy the dog work.

"There's a bird down somewhere along that ditch, Neville," Frank shouted. "See what your dog can do."

I called Rye, my German Wire-haired Pointer to heel. The last drive had brought everyone back to where we had all parked our cars. This was our first outing in company, and here we were playing to an audience of knowledgeable spectators.

I cast Rye along the ditch. He took off at an alarming rate but his athletic form suddenly froze, with nose forward, tail horizontal, foreleg raised. The classic point. The kill had been clean. He spotted the bird, picked it up, came straight back to me and executed the textbook delivery. There was a vigorous round of applause from the gallery.

A perfect end to a perfect day.

Quarrying

There's no shortage of stone in the Pennines and it's never far below the surface. There is plain evidence of this when one sees the shallow depressions which occur at intervals alongside the drystone walls in the remoter parts of the dales. It would have been an arduous task to transport walling stone to these sites from existing quarries. It was much easier to dig a hole, expose the stone beds and use the readily available material. A little further along, another mini-quarry could be established.

The dales are a geologist's paradise. A huge variety of material was available to farming and its allied industries. Dressed sandstone blocks were ideal for building the walls of the houses, byres and barns. In other quarries the sandstone occurred in strata ideal for fashioning into roof tiles or flagstones for the floors of the houses and byres. Millstone grit had an obvious use. Today you can still see half-finished millstones lying in groups where they were fashioned on the high moors a hundred years ago.

Here ganister is being quarried. It splits readily in two planes to produce excellent walling stone.

A lifetime of working the quarry has made the Scott brothers adept at handling this material. Like most experts, they make it look easy. Heavy machinery must be used to manoeuvre the large blocks into place. After that it's down to a keen eye for the natural grain in the rock and an almost telepathic co-ordination of their manual skills.

They work the quarry in all weathers. You see here the complete production team: two men working their way through a few thousand tons of rock; a third family member handles the transport.

This is the final stage in the production of the walling stone. The large rocks have been broken down into a more manageable size and must be split along two more planes to produce the shape and size suitable for walling. Again, an experienced eye and skill with the tools of the trade are required.

There has always been a healthy demand for this stone but, of late, the brothers have been busier than ever. The Country Stewardship Scheme financed with European funds, and administered by the Ministry of Agriculture, is promoting the rebuilding and renovation of stone walls. This has stimulated need for the supply of walling stone.

Having worked the quarry for most of their lives, Raymond and Colin know their stone. Some will be suitable for fashioning into "throughs" (*see page 95*) while other beds will yield normal walling stone.

Stonewalling

Most hill farmers are competent wallers and can mend "gaps" as they occur. There is over a ton of stone in every yard of wall, and the sheer weight of the structure, under the influence of gravity, dictates that it will move and subside in time.

I came across these two old boys doing their running repairs to a stretch of wall whilst I was on my rounds in the upper dale. I pulled the car onto the verge opposite where they were working, wound down the window and called to them, "Good Morning". There was no response. I was aware that they were both "hard of hearing" and so intent on their task that they did not realise that I was there, even though I was only a few yards away. Their eyes never left their work and I took several pictures without feeling that I had intruded.

Years later, long after they had gone to "the great hill farm in the sky", I was delighted to give an enlarged print of one of these pictures to their nephew who held them in great affection.

Very old walls that have subsided, become moss-clad and outlived their usefulness can become objects of fascinating beauty. As a low autumn sun hits this one at an acute angle, its texture and colour make a wonderful picture.

Left. Ken was brought up on a dales farm and can turn his hand to most of the skills and chores which he learned in his boyhood.

Nowadays he earns his living by shepherding, hedge-laying, and stone-walling, wherever there is a need for his diverse skills. Stone walling takes up most of his time. For a man with a keen interest in natural history and who loves being out in the countryside, walling is an agreeable occupation. Occasionally he finds fascinating artefacts such as ornate clay pipes left behind by the original builders more than a century before, but his real joy is his contact with the wildlife of the wall. He finds stoats' nests, mummified adders, toads and lizards, and tells a wonderful story of an encounter with a slow worm.

He came across one of the little creatures hibernating in a newly collapsed length of wall that he had been called on to repair. It was November, and he realised that in its exposed position, the slow worm would not survive the winter, so he took it home. In an outhouse he recreated a suitable environment with stone and in the spring returned the creature to exactly the same spot where he had found it. He was thrilled to see it snake its way back into the depths of the wall.

Walls in the landscape

The natural beauty of the dales landscape is awe-inspiring, but it is a man-made feature – the miles upon miles of stone walling – which adds to its character and charm.

Walling has been used since Tudor times to delineate outer and inner pastures and to segregate stock from crop-growing areas. Villagers had grazing rights on these common pastures and by the end of the eighteenth century increasing stocking rates were causing problems. Various "Enclosure Acts" between 1790 and 1845 were seen to be the solution. Each grazier on common land was allotted a specific area which he was required to enclose with walls. There was a flurry of building in the space of about fifty years and most of the walls we see today are the result. Public quarries were set up where those in need of walling materials could go to extract stone. There was no charge for this service as long as the stone was not sold for someone else's use.

Hundreds of miles of walls divide the landscape into fields and paddocks of varying sizes. Here we see a very interesting pattern. Little paddocks would be used for cultivation or penning small numbers of stock; larger fields were enclosed. Immense stretches of wall snake their way up the hillside onto the fells.

The structure of the walls is far more complex than one would imagine at first. Each wall is, in effect, two walls with an infill of loose stone between them and a row of topping stones. The base has a width of about three feet and it tapers to about sixteen inches at the top. Two or three rows of "throughs" (pronounced "thruffs") were required at intervals to bind together the outer and inner faces. In some dales the throughs were left prominent, whilst in others they were chipped to leave an even face.

Gritstone gateposts punctuate the walls as do "cripple holes" or "smout holes" which allowed sheep to pass through into the next field.

Belties

The image of the hill farmer is one who is bred to it. "Heather bred and crowdy fed" goes the saying. His family has farmed these hills for generations through good and bad times. But rules are there to be broken. Paul Coppen has been a hill farmer for a mere thirteen years and he has hit on a formula for success in these hard times.

Ignoring the trends to farm rapidly-growing, fast-maturing continental breeds he made the bizarre choice of the Belted Galloway.

The Galloway breed is not renowned for its sweet temperament but Paul has gained the trust of all his stock. Thirteen years ago he was North of England Technical Manager for ICI's Agricultural Chemicals Division. To retire from an executive post and start from scratch establishing a herd of "Belties" in a less than hospitable environment may have seemed a strange decision. However, his rationale is beyond criticism.

I quote Paul: "All my land rises to

nine hundred feet above sea level where there's hardly a tree in sight to give any shelter. This breed can live outside and forage all year round. As the weather gets colder they grow a thicker coat. The outer hairs throw off the water and underneath they have a mossy waistcoat that keeps them warm. In winter hay and straw supplement their grazing. There is a big building where they can come and go as they wish, but even in the worst weather they prefer to go out during the day and will happily eat rushes sticking out through the snow. The modern continental breeds would just stand in the shed whinging and waiting for their next meal of concentrate feed."

Because the Belted Galloway is a traditional breed it will thrive on the sparse fare of the high moorland. Paul can farm by strict organic principles and has little need for nitrogen fertiliser, pesticides or concentrate feed. Again I quote Paul: "Beef produced by modern farming methods is from animals usually around two years old whereas the Belted Galloways feeding only on grass and hay mature more slowly. By the time they are three to three and a half years old they produce really excellent quality beef. As it takes longer to raise my bullocks you do have to pay a little more. I'm convinced there is a growing market for high quality beef reared naturally from the rare breeds."

When Paul's beef was available in a local butcher's shop the owner of a top London restaurant discovered its "fine flavoursome" qualities. A tasting session was arranged for food journalists from national newspapers and "Beltie" beef was judged head and shoulders above all other contenders. The rather negative aspect of all this is that the above-mentioned London restaurant takes all the beef Paul can produce. It is no longer available locally.

Perhaps there is a lesson to be learned here.

Longhorns

The Longhorn is one of our native breeds which declined in numbers until in 1938 only a dozen bulls and about 50 cows were registered in the herd book. Fortunately a few enthusiasts saved the Longhorn from extinction, and its qualities as a commercial proposition were recognised.

The breed is slow maturing, but is hardy, produces excellent beef, and can thrive on a modest diet.

Its popularity has risen dramatically in recent years, and at some major shows it has gained prizes when competing against the more fashionable breeds. There are now 165 herds in the country, a total of nearly three thousand animals.

J Neville Fitt wrote in 1876: "Where did he come from, this singularly picturesque beast with the carriage of a lion and the temper of a dove – the one breed in which the feeder, the butcher and the artist may equally delight?"

Where indeed did the Longhorn come from? No one really knows. The Craven area of West Yorkshire was well known for some fine examples. Certainly varieties of Longhorn have been farmed for centuries, but it was Robert Bakewell, famous cattle breeder and improver, who was responsible for the appearance of the breed as we know it today.

The sturdy Longhorn calf on the left of the picture was not aware of the life and death drama he went through only two months previously.

Within a few hours of his birth he was stricken by an acute septicaemia. His decline was rapid and when I first saw him, he was virtually in a coma. Antibiotics alone would not save him. I decided to try a blood transfusion from his dam. Dodging her flailing horns, I took a pint of blood from her jugular vein and slowly dripped it into his. The stockman nursed him through the night and next day the calf was on the road to recovery.

Chiropody

In recent years the stockman has become very aware of the importance of foot care in his cattle. Lameness will seriously affect their health and welfare. Preventive foot trimming is now widely carried out by fully trained cattle "chiropodists" as a routine measure to prevent lameness.

As well as his knives and clippers, the itinerant foot trimmer brings a lightweight cattle crush to restrain the patient and raise the foot. Once raised, it is cleaned by rubbing vigorously with handfuls of sawdust which is surprisingly good at removing dirt. Water is not as efficient and has the disadvantage of leaving a wet, slippery foot with which to work.

Note that the cow and the operator are comfortable and safe. Years ago, before the advent of the foot-trimming man, veterinary surgeons did much of this work. If a crush wasn't available, a rope was tied to the cow's leg and hoisted over a roof beam. It wasn't much fun dodging a flying foot while trying to perform delicate trimming.

On one occasion the cow was kicking so hard that the roof beam came down and nearly killed me!

The initial work is done with farrier's clippers. It is a sound practice to take small bites since it is very easy to cut into the "quick". Special attention is paid to the side walls and the toe area. A foot with a long toe will tend to make the cow walk with much of her weight thrown back on her heels and this affects the posture of the whole limb. Most problems concern the outside claw of the hind foot because that one takes more than its fair share of the bovine's weight.

Having sorted out the general shape of the foot with the clippers, the operator takes the hoof knife to add the finishing touches.

The hoof knife is obviously purpose-designed. It can be double edged and the blade curves back on itself at the end so that the operator can cut into corners. It needs to be made of good quality steel. A poor quality material will soon lose its edge dealing with the tough horn of a cow's foot and I've been reminded several times that it's easier to cut yourself with a blunt knife than a sharp one. (With a blunt knife you have to exert more force and are very likely to slip.)

The main operation with the hoof knife is the paring away of excess horn depth on the sole. Again it is important to take off small slivers with each stroke of the blade to avoid cutting into the sensitive inner structures.

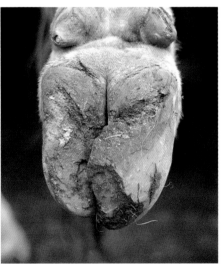

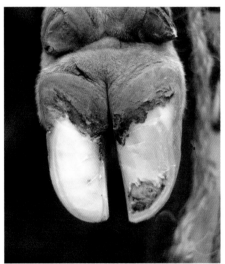

All my own work. This is the hind foot of a very large Charolais bull. It was touch and go whether or not he would fit into the cattle crush. I just had to take "before" and "after" pictures, as I knew the difference would be remarkable. The outer claw of the hind foot bears a lot of weight, especially in such a heavy animal, and the excessive pressure has resulted in exuberant horn growth in much the same way as when we develop hard skin or corns on our feet.

This is instant job satisfaction. Actually it wasn't instant because it took about 20 minutes and quite an effort. Horn clippings littered the floor but I'd resurrected something near to a normal-shaped bovine foot. Sound hind feet, as you can imagine, are very important in a stock bull.

Gathering

The hill sheep spend much of their life out on the fell but at certain times of the year will be "gathered" and brought down to the farmstead. The major gatherings are for clipping, weaning, and (as here) for tupping time in the autumn. The ewes will be checked for condition, sound teeth and sound udders before they qualify for next year's breeding programme.

The big gatherings are planned like military operations and involve as many men, dogs and quad bikes as can be mustered. The team sets off before first light and may not return before dark. The weather forecast is critical. Driving rain or a sudden thick fog could be disastrous.

It's a tough enough trip for the men, but the dogs are amazing. They never stop, and are almost as fresh at the end of the day as they were at the start.

It's an impressive sight watching the flock arrive at the farmstead. The horizon suddenly fills with sheep and they come down the hillside in a woolly cascade, which streams through the gate. Even before the days of mobile phones, the family would have some idea of when they would be back and would come out to greet them. I suppose nowadays the shepherd could ring home to ask his wife to put the kettle on!

Poultry

I really could not hazard a guess at the number of farmyards I have visited, but each has an ambience of its own. My favourites by far are those with a rich assortment of chickens, ducks and geese which add character and colour to the scene.

The poultry are traditionally fed and watered by the farmer's wife. They are her preserve, and the nursery book picture of her in her apron scattering largesse to the ever-hungry birds is, to some extent, accurate.

Chickens were first domesticated about 5000 years ago in India. They were in Egypt by 1400BC and arrived in Britain about 2000 years ago. The plumage and colour pattern of the cock bird illustrated here is very much like that of the Indian Jungle Fowl from which modern poultry were bred.

All domestic fowl can interbreed to produce some weird and wonderful crosses. Poultry enthusiasts who preserve the old bloodlines must pen their pure-bred stock separately to ensure pure-bred offspring. I suspect that this handsome fellow has some "Old English Game Fowl" in his ancestry.

This fellow has survived a few Christmases but what has been missed at the dinner table has been amply compensated for by the colour and character he's added to the farmyard. When a turkey cock is in full display mode he's quite a sight.

In the whole of my career I've never seen anything so funny as a drunken duck. He waddled bizarrely, quacked dementedly, and fell over at regular intervals. He'd been feeding in an orchard on well-fermented apples. He was hospitalised, treated, and left next morning with what looked like a major hangover.

Geese along with Guinea Fowl make great security devices in the farmyard. They are very territorial and should anyone invade their space they give voice fortissimo. An attack by an enraged gander is an unnerving experience. They hiss, extend their necks aggressively and flap their wings alarmingly. It's wise to retreat.

The farm sale

Years ago I was at a farm sale and a man from a nearby town engaged me in conversation. This was the first time he had attended such a sale and expressed his incredulity at the high prices that the lots were realising. "This second-hand stuff is making more than it would if it were new," he said. I explained that this was because his neighbours held the vendor in high regard. "They're all here," I added "and they'll all want to buy something. By encouraging vigorous bidding they're making sure he has a good send off. It's a token of respect."

As the vendor is retiring from farming, everything must go. He'll be leaving the farm so none of it is any good to him in retirement. The "deadstock" (as opposed to "livestock") is hauled out into a convenient field for display. The auctioneer will have made an inventory in the weeks prior to the sale. Everything will have some value, even if it is to the scrap metal merchants who are always much in evidence.

It's a long day, so there's usually a mobile canteen in attendance doing a brisk trade in bacon rolls and mugs of steaming tea.

An auction ring has been constructed in the farmyard. The cattle have all been labelled with their lot numbers, and the vendor is in the ring as each of them comes through. He'll move them gently round the ring to show them off and is also in a position to prompt the auctioneer to announce any points which will encourage potential bidders.

The auctioneer has put in a lot of hard work in the weeks running up to the sale. He has organised the date, catalogued all the lots and advertised the details in the local press. All that remains now is to encourage some animated bidding. His clerk will make a note of all the successful bids and secretarial staff will prepare the purchasers' accounts promptly.

The agricultural show

Throughout the summer and into early autumn, members of the practice give up their free time to do the "Hon Vet" duties at a long list of events ranging from pet shows to hunter trials. Whenever possible I would opt for the duties at the agricultural shows. This was partly because of my place in the cornet section of the village band, but also because I enjoyed the "buzz" of these grand annual get-togethers.

Going to a village show always reminds me of going to a wedding in that you know exactly what the format will be, you'll know a lot of the faces there, and you know you'll enjoy it. And like a wedding, much depends on the weather.

Arranging an outdoor event in the British climate is an act of faith, and no one is more aware of this than the show committee. Throughout the year they have held fund-raising social events to top up reserves. In the weeks preceding the show, volunteers have knocked on doors in the dale selling "subscriptions" (a euphemism for non-returnable advance ticket sales) to provide further insurance against financial disaster. It's always a great relief when show day dawns dry and bright.

A day at the agricultural show has so many things to offer. For some it's the opportunity to show off prize stock, garden produce or craftsmanship. For others it may be the competition in the horse and pony sections. Some merely come to be entertained.

But for many it's just a great social occasion: a grand gathering of dales folk; an opportunity to get together with friends, some of whom you haven't seen since you met them at last year's show.

The five northern counties have always had a strong tradition of goat keeping and the popularity of the goat sections at the shows bears witness to this fact. Rural cottagers, miners and railwaymen often kept a goat, and the hill farmer knows how useful a goat can be when there are pet lambs to be fed.

Since Tudor times goats had been kept on board ships to supply fresh milk and meat on long voyages. During the Victorian era, when the British Empire was at its height, the shipboard goat provided sustenance for crews and passengers. Hundreds of goats arrived from exotic lands, and, at the turn of the century, goat enthusiasts imported some Swiss stock. This accounts for the cosmopolitan nature of today's British goat population.

Here we see an Anglo-Nubian on the left, a Toggenberg in the centre and a British Alpine on the right.

Whilst many agricultural shows have developed into country fairs with all manner of displays and events to attract the general public, the village show at Bowes steadfastly remains a hill farmer's show. I can imagine that it has not changed greatly since the first one was held well over a hundred years ago.

Sheep classes figure prominently. It is the Mecca for the Pennine hill farmers who breed the sturdy Swaledale sheep. This is, in effect, their world championship and the show is often referred to as the "Swaledale Royal". Winning the tup shearling trophy at Bowes could be equated with winning the Grand National. Given the choice, I know which piece of hardware these folk would prefer to pick up.

Winter

At least once, and usually several times during the winter, the upper dales look like this. The snowploughs open the roads; it's all very pretty, and usually harmless. However, 1947, 1963 and 1979 were legendary for the severity of the storms and the hardship suffered by the farmer and his stock. Even now, after twenty relatively mild winters, there are always a month's provisions in the farmhouse during the winter months in case a sudden storm strikes.

One family has vivid memories of '63. They were seriously cut off. The children didn't get to school between Christmas and Easter. At one point the only way out of the house was to crawl out of the bedroom window and slide down a fourteen-foot snowdrift. Every day the family's task was to go out and search for sheep "overblown" and buried in snowdrifts. One sheep was pulled out alive after three weeks under the snow.

The daily fare was "potato hash" with whatever could be found to flavour it. Eventually things were desperate and an airdrop was arranged. Hay sweepings were gathered into a pile near the farmhouse and set alight to act as a beacon. A large transport aircraft flew low and dropped diesel fuel, coal, provisions and hay.

Retrieving the goods scattered in the arctic conditions was a major task.

Severe winters would seem to be a thing of the past. Is it global warming? Or is it just good luck?

Dramatic tales are told about past winters in the days when cattle were still wintered in fieldhouses distant from the farmstead and the hill farmer faced a daily trek to feed and water his stock. Nowadays the cattle are housed in large, purpose-built sheds near to the farmhouse. Fodder can be handled mechanically in the form of big round bales that are stored conveniently close by.

The stark majestic beauty of the dale clad in a covering of deep fresh snow is awesome, but it does pose serious problems for the hill farmer. Sheep still spend the winter on the fell and, should a storm strike, their welfare would be a major problem. The modern mechanical farm has not yet produced a device for locating and digging out overblown sheep.

In recent years the main problem has been rain. It has fallen until the ground could no longer absorb what was coming down. Cold "clashy" weather is the main enemy of the hill farmer these days. It is stressful to him and his stock.

The winter landscape

Snowfall like this looks lovely but it can make life difficult. January 1979 saw the first of four violent snowstorms that crippled the area for three months. On the night the storm struck I received a call from the upper dale: "We've got a cow that we think is having trouble calving. There's no way you'll get here tonight but will you try in the morning?"

The following morning I arranged for a four-wheel-drive vehicle to ferry two of us as near to the farm as possible. We packed a rucksack with emergency rations and everything we could possibly need for a bovine obstetric case. The two mile trek through waist-deep snow was arduous. The calving case, though successful, was physically exhausting. The return trip wasn't much fun either, although mugs of coffee and slabs of excellent Christmas cake had fortified us.

We had set out at first light and returned to the rendezvous with our transport after dark. The warm glow of thawing out was accentuated by thoughts of a job well done.

The high fells in the background of this picture were the scene of a near fatal drama some years ago.

Returning home from a visit to a neighbouring dale, one of our clients who lived in a particularly remote farm was caught in a sudden blizzard. When he had set off on the outward journey the weather was fine. There was no hint of what was to come. On the return trip in the early evening he met snow and, some way along the track to the farm, had to abandon his vehicle. He continued his journey on foot but the snow got deeper. Powdery flakes swirled round in the wind, causing "white-out" conditions and he lost his bearings completely.

He realised the danger of wandering off in an aimless direction on the treacherous fell, but also realised that he had to keep moving; so he planted his stick in the snow and walked around it all night. His wife rode their pony out into the storm to look for him, but wisely did not dare to venture out onto the fell in those conditions.

At first light he regained his bearings and managed to complete the journey home.

A weather forecast that mentions snow evokes unpleasant memories for the hill farmer: memories of trudging through it, waist-deep, to the off buildings, or of digging out dozens of overblown sheep.

But he'd be the first to acknowledge the beauty of a fresh snowfall.

Fieldhouses

The fieldhouse is essentially a stone barn with a hayloft above and a cow byre below. Cattle used to spend the whole of the winter in these buildings. There must be thousands of them scattered round our dales and each is different. In some areas it seems that every field has one. Professional planners played no part in their solid, enduring construction. Common sense and function were the most important considerations.

Fieldhouses come in all shapes and sizes. Some are of cathedral-like proportions whilst others, like this one, are more modest. The styles of architecture seem to carry their own stamp from dale to dale. Consider the flamboyant "throughs" of Swaledale, the prominent quoins of Stainmore, the rigid perpendiculars of Teesdale, and the paler limestone building materials of Wharfedale. I've often thought that a connoisseur of the dales could be dropped by parachute and would instantly recognise which dale he'd landed in as soon as he came upon a fieldhouse.

This is a fieldhouse on the grander scale with two byres, two haylofts, and a huge central doorway for backing in a trailer and unloading the hay. It never ceases to amaze me that these structures are so substantial and well built. The lines are so clean and straight. There is no sign of subsidence or decay. The stone slabs which tile the roof must weigh many tons but are all level and in place. The design is of the "no frills" variety and our parachutist would have no hesitation in placing it in Teesdale.

I have passed this fieldhouse hundreds of times and puzzled over the high wall on the western side. What was its purpose? Perhaps it gave shelter from the fierce prevailing winds when handling loose hay or letting the cattle out to drink at the trough.

It was in a fieldhouse such as this where I faced one of my most spectacular near-to-death experiences. Veterinary surgeons in large animal practice face these at regular, though not too frequent, intervals. To conduct my examination I needed to squeeze between my patient and her neighbour in a double stall. Both had seemed docile until I was in position, but then one of the pair panicked.

Suddenly there was I, sandwiched between two demented cows. All hell broke loose. Both were striking at me from both ends. Well-aimed kicks from their hind feet thundered into my thighs while their heads were intent on butting me into oblivion.

Adrenalin must have taken over, for I felt no pain. I observed calmly that there was no safe way out of this predicament. If I lost my footing it would be the end.

The crazed animals would kick and stamp until every bone in my body was broken.

And then a rope touched my head. The farmer had realised that there was no escape at ground level but had noticed that I was directly under the trapdoor to the hayloft. I was hauled to safety like a Peter Pan flying through the air in wellies!

A typical dales landscape with fieldhouses and drystone walls. Although the fieldhouse system was incredibly labour intensive by modern standards, its practicality was admirable. Fieldhouses are always situated in hay meadows where, in summer, the grass would be cut to provide winter feed for the stock. When the hay was satisfactorily made, horse-drawn sweeps and sledges would gather it in loose piles at the foot of the wall of the fieldhouse below the "forking hole". Using a pitchfork, a skilled man would launch the hay through this small door into the hayloft, where it would be carefully spread and trodden down.

In the winter, tranches could be cut away and dropped through a trapdoor to the cattle in the byre below. Manure from the dung channel or "grip" behind the animals could be brushed to the lower end of the building and shovelled through a small window onto the dungheap or "midden". In the spring this could be spread onto the land to ensure a vigorous hay crop the following year. While the grass was growing in the spring and summer, the cattle would be grazing the high pastures.

Even with advancing mechanisation in the first half of the twentieth century and the practice of baling hay the fieldhouse system was a simple strategy in dales farming. The only major drawback was that at least once a day, during winter, the hill farmer had to tour the far reaches of his land to feed and water his stock.

Sadly the fieldhouses are becoming redundant but they remain as an integral part of our dales landscape and a monument to the hardy souls who farmed this land.

This is the interior of an old fieldhouse, long disused: wooden partitions separate each double stall and the cows in them were kept apart by the stone partitions. The latter are bigger than you would imagine, for like an iceberg, there is more below the surface than above. The hayracks are wooden.

Traditionally the area where the cows lay (the "boose") was cobbled and the passageway paved with stone flagstones. Between was the dung channel locally known as the "grip" or "group". In some of the dales, sods of earth were placed at the front of the boose to cushion the cows' knees when lying down or standing up.

Many of the traditional names for the structures in the fieldhouse originate from the Norse settlers and are probably recognisable by modern Scandinavians.

At the lower end of the fieldhouse, at a convenient height up the wall, is the "mucking hole". The term is self-explanatory. The contents of the dung channel behind the cows could be swept to the lower end wall, shovelled out through this hole onto the "midden" and then spread over the field in the late winter or early spring before the grass started to grow.

Our eponymous hero was a hard worker, yes, but he was no fool. You will notice that fieldhouses are seldom tucked neatly into the corner of a field. They stand right in the centre. If one is bringing in hay and spreading muck, it's easier to work from the middle.

This fieldhouse is built, like many, on a sloping hillside. The strategy of the pragmatic dalesman is clear. It's so much easier to fork the hay into the top side and to shovel the manure out of the bottom end. It's also clear that its useful days are over. The farmer now has large cattle sheds near to the farmstead and can use his foreloader to bring fodder to his stock.

This is one of my favourites. It stands in a typical dales pasture liberally sprinkled with rushes and bog-loving flora. Its original *raison d'être* has long gone; the cow stalls disappeared many years ago. The ground floor accommodation now provides shelter for sheep in the winter months. It stands high on a hillside and has a wonderful, grand, outside staircase.

Bedding and feeding

Fieldhouses and byres don't adapt well to the modern mechanical farm. This is a typical "big building" and almost every hill farmer has erected something similar in the last fifteen to twenty years. Most of the space inside is devoted to large cattle yards and there is a gangway wide enough to allow a tractor to deposit hay or silage rations into the feeding area. Cattle can reach through a barrier to feed. Hay bales may be stored inside or bagged silage in the open nearby. One man can handle the whole operation.

What could be simpler than this feeding system? The young stock are accommodated in a building where they can shelter indoors or come out into a yard. When they have almost finished the food in front of them, another silage bale is placed by the feed barrier. Partial unrolling will ensure that it is available along the length of the barrier.

If hay and silage are handled in big bales, then it makes sense for bedding materials to take the same form. Hill farmers used to make round trips of fifty miles or more at harvest time to bring trailer loads of straw in small bales from the lowland arable farms.

A few deliveries of big bales are quicker and cheaper and can be unrolled as if laying a carpet.

Left. Winter rations. The precarious business of haymaking is still important but virtually all cattle, and some sheep, feed on silage in the winter. In the few years that this form of preserved food has been used, there have been developments and improvements. Originally big black bags were used. If rabbits gnawed through these and let air in, the whole bale could be spoiled. However, nowadays a rather clever machine can wrap the big bales in a substance not unlike domestic "clingfilm". Occasionally rabbits will tear the wrapping but because it is so closely applied the damage to the contents is localised.

Lead mining

Lead mining has played its part in the history of the Dales since at least Roman times. The flurry of activity in the 18th and 19th centuries was marked by great feats of water engineering. Aqueducts criss-crossed the fells, diverting streams to power water wheels deep inside the mines. Dams were built on the high ground, and water would be repeatedly released from them to wash away topsoil and expose the lead-veins. This latter practice called "hushing" resulted in a lattice of steep sided man-made valleys in the mining landscape. A low sun or a dusting of snow throws the hushes into sharp relief.

Sheep portraits

The Swaledale tup has a handsome head, and the connoisseur knows all the nuances that will bring success in the show ring. The shape must be right, with the set of the jaw giving good alignment of the teeth. The black pigmented hairs must stop sharply when they meet the white muzzle. The texture of the hair on the forehead should be good; wiry but with a nice springy feel.

The light in the dales is ever changing, and as one travels, the horizon changes with the irregular contours of the landscape. When the winter sun is low, a journey presents a feast for the eyes, a non-stop series of dramatic silhouettes. Here a sturdy Swaledale tup breaks up the skyline.

From its humble beginnings as one of the hardy, horned, native breeds of hill sheep that had adapted to life in the harsh environment of the high Pennines, the Swaledale breed has risen to a position of distinction over the last hundred years.

Their hardy nature, sturdy body, thick weatherproof fleece and ability to thrive on the most meagre of rations are qualities that have been influential in their success. A formal breed society was not set up until 1919. The fact that the breed is an ancient one is borne out by the conditions for registration in the first *Flock Book*. Only animals that had been bred true for twenty-five years would be admitted. The society has improved the breed tremendously in its eighty-year existence. Tups that are to be used to sire pedigree stock are approved only after a rigorous inspection.

You can't travel far in the Pennines without seeing a Swaledale sheep. There are now over one and a half million in the British Isles. Add to that the fact that the most popular cross-bred ewe is the North of England Mule (bred out of the Swaledale) with numbers exceeding four million, and we come to the conclusion that almost a third of all breeding sheep in the UK carry Swaledale blood.

Quad bikes

Someone once described the quad bike as the biggest revolution in sheep farming since the "invention" of the collie dog.

Before its arrival, if the shepherd couldn't get there by tractor, it was all legwork. Gathering even a small flock of sheep from a limited area of moor could be an all-day job and would involve help from friends and neighbours. With the quad bike such a task can be accomplished in less than half the time and with a quarter of the manpower.

The machines appeared in this area in the early 80s and had three wheels. Everyone thought they were the ultimate till someone had the bright idea of adding an extra wheel. It was only then that it was realised how unstable the three-wheelers had been. The standard four wheeler is virtually essential on any hill farm nowadays, enabling the farmer to achieve much more in his busy working day.

There have been further developments since the introduction of the fourth wheel: panniers on front and back enable transport of bulky loads and a trailer can be attached to a hitch on the back. This is particularly useful since it is big enough to transport large quantities of fodder or carry a sick ewe from the moor for treatment back at the farmstead.

In winter it can be a chilly ride. Built-in gauntlets on the handlebar controls of most models provide limited protection from cold winds, but this is the ultimate in quad bike comfort.

Haircuts

Before: Cattle grow a heavy winter coat in this part of the world and, traditionally, heads, bellies and tails are shaved before the animals are presented for sale. This is quite a skilled task.

After: The cattle do look much more civilised when they have been "clipped out".

To give a haircut to a young, excitable, recently-weaned suckler calf a good cattle crush is essential. The crush should have a good head restraint and safe access at the sides and the back. To expedite the procedure, two sets of electric clippers are useful: one man can clip the head while another does the body.

The calves tolerate the interference quite well and the head can be neatly shaved. Tidying up the tail and tail head is straightforward. Clipping along the underside of the belly is the tricky bit. A sudden kick as the operator reaches forward can do serious damage.

Testing

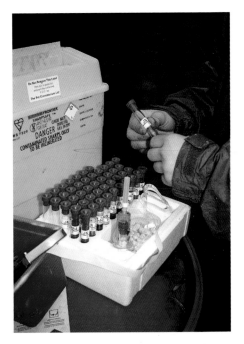

Diligent attention to the paperwork is necessary when TB testing or blood sampling. All cattle have ear tags which carry their unique identification number. This, and the cow's details, are recorded. Blood tubes are carefully labelled. Used needles are safely disposed of in special containers.
It's a good idea to get most of the testing schedule completed in the winter when the cattle are housed.

Many years ago tuberculosis in cattle was a major problem, not only because it was debilitating to the animals, but also because it could be transmitted to man. The Ministry of Agriculture initiated an eradication programme many years ago. The scheme is based on a skin test, which is being carried out here. Tiny amounts of "tuberculin" are injected into the cow's neck and the reaction assessed in 72 hours. TB is now very uncommon in this part of the world, but all adult cattle are still subjected to the test once every four years.

Dales Ponies

For years ponies like this one were an essential part of the hill farm. Under the saddle they were the shepherd's mode of transport. Between the shafts they would pull carts, agricultural machinery and sledges. In hand they could carry enormous weights slung on each side. Their versatility, capacity for hard work, surefootedness and steady temperament were ideal. Stories are told of incredible feats of endurance pulling sledges filled with hay through deep snow to the sheep on the hill.

Their specific history is obscured by time, but without doubt their origins lie with the "Scotch Galloway", a sturdy breed from the south west of Scotland. There are hints of Clydesdale in their powerful and muscular hindquarters, and there is a touch of the Hackney in their elegant trotting gait.

Their origins are inextricably linked with those of the Fell Pony of the western Pennines and there has been much heated argument on that subject. In the 1920s there were reports of a stallion winning a championship in the "Dales" section of a prestigious show and his full brother winning a "Fell" championship. Happily these differences have been sorted out and both societies continue to flourish.

Richie Longstaff was brought up with Dales Ponies. His father was one of a band of enthusiasts who helped to save the breed from almost certain extinction in the 1950s. Throughout the flourishing years of the lead industry in the 19th century and well into the 20th century when tractors appeared, ponies like these were the basic power unit in the Pennines. There must have been thousands used for everyday tasks in the lead mines and on the hill farms, but as the need for their services declined, so their numbers dwindled.

In 1955 there were only four registrations in the Dales Pony Society studbook. In 1977 the Rare Breeds Survival Trust was alerted to the situation. It was shortly after this that Richie resurrected the family tradition and started breeding Dales Ponies.

He and his wife, Freda, have a great affection for the breed. They have had success in the show ring and there is a constant demand for their foals. A few years ago a gentleman from Oregon read about the Dales Pony and contacted the breed society. They put him in touch with the Longstaffs, who sold him four foals, which were, as far as we know, the first Dales Ponies in the USA.

Stickmaking

The shepherd's crook is essentially a working tool. It can be used to catch and restrain a sheep. It can be used as a walking stick when traversing uneven ground, and is a useful probe when searching for sheep "overblown" in a snowstorm. Hazel and holly are favoured materials for the shanks whilst handles can be wood or horn. The craftsmanship involved in embellishment of the handles has developed into a veritable art form and many a long winter's evening is devoted to "stickdressing".

This is a remarkable piece of craftsmanship. It is made from a single piece of hazel. Once the right piece of wood has been found and cut, it must be left for at least a year to dry out and "season". If the wood or drying conditions are less than perfect the wood can split.

After carving the elegant handle, the maker spends hours working on it to achieve the beautiful finish.

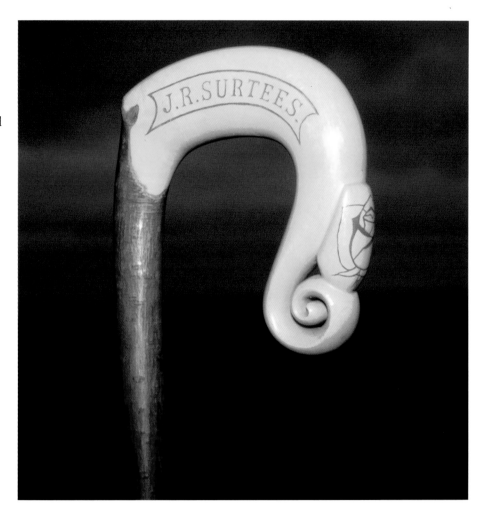

The making of a stick like this takes a lot of time and patience. The right shaped horn must be found, seasoned, gently heated and pressed to reduce the natural curve to a single plane, carved, decorated, and "married" to a suitable shank. The horn is from a Swaledale tup, the decoration is a red grouse, and it was made by a noted craftsman, Jack Walton, of Newton Lodge.

Another Jack Walton stick.

I was determined that my retirement should be a low profile, no ballyhoo, no parties affair. However, one evening my wife, Chris, whisked me away to a hotel at the top of the dale and into a surprise party organised by some of the farmers up there.

"Well if I'm to get a present, I hope it's a horn-handled stick," I said to Chris.

It was. And to my delight, it was made by Jack Walton.

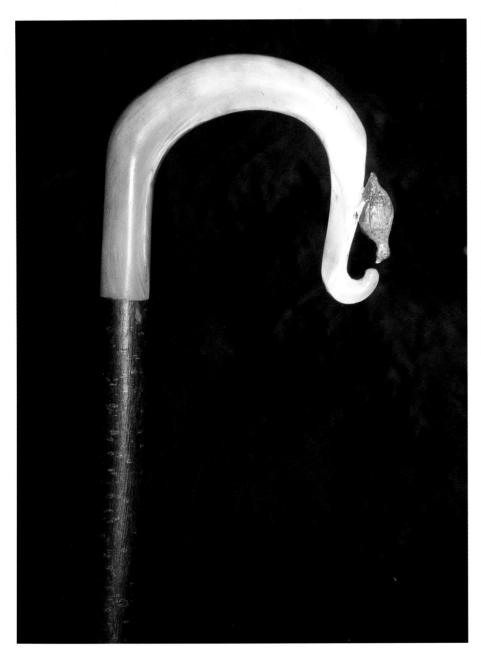

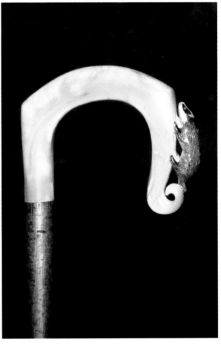

Lime

The burning of limestone must have been of major importance in the dales for hundreds of years. There are limekilns everywhere. This one is on the high moors just south of Reeth. They were obviously built where there was a ready supply of suitable stone, for there is always evidence of quarrying adjacent to the kilns.

I had always assumed that the lime was used entirely for land improvement, but there also must have been a high demand for its use in mortar for building, and in whitewash.

The limekilns were packed with alternating layers of fuel and nuggets of limestone. Until the coming of the railways wood was the main fuel but when coke became available, it was probably preferred.

After a good blaze was started in the bottom layer of fuel, the burn would take about a week to run its course. As the contents of the burn settled, more stone was added.

A good burn would leave a load of evenly-powdered quicklime, but if less than successful the centre of the nuggets held a lump of unburned stone. These were referred to as "bucks".

It must have been a laborious business, transporting lime away from the old kilns by the individual cartload to the farm where it was spread by hand. Although a few of the old kilns were used until a few decades ago, they are now all redundant. Today, processed limestone arrives from outside the dale in huge wagons and is spread quickly and efficiently with specialised equipment.

Lime is still applied to the land for soil conditioning, although vast amounts were used historically in the creation of "intakes" – a farm bordering the moor could extend its useful grazing land by treating a patch of adjoining heather moor. The land was first "pared" – the removal of the sward, either physically or by overgrazing. Remaining vegetation was burned off, drains were laid then large quantities of manure and lime applied to complete the operation.

The intakes are easily seen in any dales landscape like walled, green bites taken out of the dark heather moor.

Suckler cattle

Hill cattle production is based on the "single suckler" system. A calf is born in the spring, suckled through the summer and then weaned and sold on for intensive "finishing" in the autumn. Traditionally the dam is a beef breed/dairy breed cross, which produces a cow with a strong frame and a good supply of milk. Until the 1960s she was crossed with one of the British beef breeds such as a Hereford or Aberdeen Angus bull. After that date the beef herds gained a Continental flavour. Most beef cattle these days have a French sire. Limousin, Charolais and Blonde d'Aquitaine are the favourites but the Belgian Blue and Simmental from Switzerland are popular too.

As well as running a traditional beef suckler herd, there are some dales farmers who also keep a small herd of pedigree cattle. This is a group of pedigree Charolais calves. There will be a high demand for the bull calves to be used as sires in commercial herds.

In spite of the dominance of the Continental breeds the white faces of Hereford crosses are still to be seen in the dales. They are a hardy breed with a thick coat and can happily spend the winter out of doors in a sheltered pasture.

The rural school

Whilst hundreds of village schools have closed in recent years, this rural one, (it's not even a village school as there's no village there), has survived to serve a thinly populated upper dale. There were two such schools in the dale until 1950 when the other closed.

It caters for about twenty pupils and has two teachers, one looking after the four to seven year olds, and the other the seven to eleven year olds. A cook, a caretaker and a part-time secretary comprise the support staff. It has a remarkable claim to continuity in the community, having been there, in the same building, since 1863. Generations of farming families have attended and existing records and journals from the earliest days offer a unique insight into the history of the dale.

In this picture the children can be seen arriving at the school. Most, of course, come by Land Rover, essential in this terrain. The building is in an elevated position on the northern slopes of the dale. The view to the south and the west is breathtaking, encompassing the crags and fells of the high Pennines. There cannot be a school anywhere in the country in such a setting. An entry in the school journal in 1863 states: "It is a wild country at great elevation above sea level, its height being one thousand, two hundred and forty feet."

Some things never change. Only a few weeks ago, (as I write), a sudden storm hit the upper dale. As the weather deteriorated, it was considered prudent to send the children home at midday. An entry in the school journal dated December 3rd 1863 states: "Today a storm took us by surprise and as only one scholar had his dinner with him we were obliged to close the school at noon."

Here the pupils are setting off on a "nature walk". They could go in any direction and witness a wealth of natural history and natural beauty. However, on this expedition they were even more privileged. Two members of staff from the conservancy body, English Nature, were able to accompany them to impart their technical knowledge. A further bonus was the presence of Julie Ward, a poet working in conjunction with English Nature, who was able to increase the children's awareness of the aesthetics of the experience.

The objective of the walk, little more than a mile from the school, was something special too. It was the largest ancient juniper forest in England. The weather was ideal and numerous stops were made to draw the pupils' attention to interesting features. At the juniper forest the English Nature staff explained in detail the conservancy measures needed to preserve the unique ecology.

They would have been horrified to read the school journal for September 11th 1867. It records: "Sent the scholars at ten o clock to Juniper Scar to get juniper bushes for firewood."

The hut

This is the Marwood and Langleydale Community Centre, to use its posh name; but for miles around it's known affectionately as "The Hut". It was built in the early fifties, and had a grand opening on the 2nd of June 1953 to coincide with Coronation Day. "My word we had a real do," says one who was there and remembers it well. "The place was packed. The heavens opened but it didn't matter. Jean Stoddart and Alwyn Cross won prizes in the fancy dress, and John Stoddart was dressed as the Cisco Kid."

Its modest appearance belies its cosy, well-cared-for interior and has been well used since its auspicious opening "do". It has been the venue for dances, whist drives, Young Farmers' Club meetings, 21st birthday parties and silver and golden wedding celebrations.

A management committee of twelve is very enthusiastic about the future, and has recently been awarded a grant of £83,700 from the National Lottery. The cash will be used to build an extension, re-roof the whole building, tarmac the car park, provide access for the disabled and erect new gates.

A domino drive is held almost weekly throughout the winter months. They are always well attended, attracting folk from all the neighbouring villages. Whilst it's fun to win a prize, the main object is to have a good social evening.

In any village hall or community centre it seems there's a happy band of "tea ladies". After the domino drive, it wouldn't seem right to go home without having a cup of tea, sandwiches, home-made cakes, and biscuits.

Church and chapel

The building in the foreground of this vast landscape, believe it or not, is a Methodist Chapel. It's been closed for many years, but can you imagine the faithful making their way on foot from surrounding farms in conditions like this to attend worship?

Occasionally, in such weather, I considered it prudent to leave my car on the main road and continue my journey to the farmstead on foot. On one such trip, having trudged through the snow for about half a mile and attended to my patient, I surveyed the landscape to plan my best route back to the car. I decided to walk along the wall tops that protruded from the snow.

Of course I slipped. Arms and legs akimbo, I sank about four feet. Unable to move, I lay flat on my back and gazed at a patch of sky shaped exactly like me! I giggled. It was as though the snow was a big sheet of gingerbread and someone had punched out a life-sized gingerbread man. The farmer had been very thoughtful and observed my progress. When I had disappeared and not reappeared he feared the worst and forged his way through the snow to rescue me.

Right. This is the church of St James the Less in the parish of Forest and Frith. It must be one of the most remote parish churches in the country. True there are farms all around it but the nearest village is several miles away. Like a stone sentinel it stands alone on a knoll keeping silent vigil over the dale.

The Christmas Eve carol service is magic! The church is always packed to capacity. Folk have left their warm firesides and braved the biting wind to be there. The village band accompanies all the carols and at the end of the service plays a short concert of seasonal music while coffee, sandwiches, cakes and mince pies are served in the pews.

Emerging from the church to see a sharp frost or a dusting of snow, you just know that Christmas has arrived.